Searching For A Place

Bill Kelly

THE LEINSTER EXPRESS,
Portlaoise and Tullamore

THE LEINSTER EXPRESS.
Dublin Road, Portlaoise, Co. Laois, Ireland.
and Bridge Street, Tullamore, Co. Offaly, Ireland.

British Library Cataloguing in Publication Data

Searching For A Place
Bill Kelly

Short Stories
Miscellany of Times Past, People, Places, Observations

ISBN 0 86335 004 6

Cover photograph courtesy of Bord Fáilte.

Typesetting and Design by
Leinster Express Newspapers Ltd.

We sat under an old thorn-tree
And talked away the night,
Told all that had been said or done
Since first we saw the light.

                              W.B. Yeats.

In memory of Murphy

Contents

Continued . . .

Contents

Searching for a Place

"I will arise and go now." Well, maybe not quite yet, and most likely not to Innisfree. Not that I have anything against the place, apart from the fact that it rains far more often in the west. I keep dreaming of the Dingle Peninsula, of that long wide beach at Inch, where some of 'Ryan's Daughter' was filmed. Of the quiet winding road that hugs the cliffs, and of the Atlantic, snapping at its walls hundreds of feet below. I remember a little coffee shop and then the tip of the peninsula at Slea Head, like the end of the known world, and sitting out there in the Atlantic, the dark humps of the Blaskets, next stop the U.S. of A.

I am not a Kerryman, my roots lie closer to David Bellamy's country, the soft brown bogs in the heart of the midlands. A man could be excused for dreaming of Kerry, it's an easy place to dream about. Necessity and circumstances and a sackful of other reasons, send us all down various roads. These same roads and the destinations they bring us to would quite often be other than our own choosing, they are the jig-saws that were never quite completed. You see, here I am in the middle years and I'm discovering the truth in the old saying, "you can take the man from the bog but you can't take the bog from the man."

Dublin is a fine city, maybe it's a bit tattered at the edges, and perhaps even at the centre. But there it sits with the mountains guarding all along one side and the sea washing its feet all along the other. I often think of all the days I stood on far-flung foreign shores and wished I could walk down O'Connell Street. It wouldn't have mattered if I didn't know anyone I met, or if no-one knew me, all I wanted was to be there in my town among my people.

That has all been long done and the water now needs further dilution, the bogs are calling again, the wheel seems to have gone full circle. It's hard to explain the feeling, this necessity to live someplace where one can take in the whole scene, you a part of everything and everything a part of you. A good friend keeps telling me that in every street in the city is a village, if only I would open my eyes. But that street is attached to the next and so on to a thousand others, and I couldn't look on any of them as a village, no more than I could look at a finger and think of it as a whole person.

Like Martin Luther King, "I have a dream," and it's a little place, somewhere out there, where everyone knows everyone else, where some

7

love you and some hate you, where there's one shop, one pub and a post office and all draw their water from the same well. The day a child is born they all know, and they all come to see. The day a man dies they all walk with him along his last mile and, as they walk, the talk is of cattle and hay and the dead don't mind, for they too had their hour walking behind others and talking of cattle and hay. It's a world of nothing and a world of everything, you spread your arms and you enfold it all. When you move you make a ripple and it reaches the extremities of your horizons. In the city horizons reach to infinity, neither your ripples nor the next persons ever reach each other, they are lost in the vastness.

My city friends will feel the reverse, and think, what nonsense. They are happy in the close packed concrete and their ripples do reach each other. But for me the pull of the hills keeps calling and the wide open spaces are ever inviting. I want to stretch my arms and touch nothing, to stand and listen, to hear the roll of the sea without the background hum of a city. To look at a starry sky without the interference of street lamps. To watch the moon race through the clouds on a stormy night. To see the light in my neighbours window across the valley, at arms length and yet within the circle.

Perhaps its a search for identity, a return to source. A friend of mine, a New Yorker, tells me he feels the same thing in a different way. His dreams are of immersing himself in the streets of Manhattan, of feeling the pulse of Time Square, of being part of perhaps the most cosmopolitan piece of this earth. His eyes light up when he thinks of the day he'll return there. Such a dream is almost beyond comprehension to me, still, to each his own. As is said in modern parlance, "whatever turns you on." For me that turn-on is in some small place, yet unknown to me, but it's most likely a place where the Atlantic comes rolling in and in the woods beyond there is perpetually, the sound of silence.

— O —

Memories of Murphy

MURPHY was a small farmer, tall and lean and of the easy going variety. He would never have offended the dawn by being up before it, and being out after sunset should always be for pleasure and not for business. There was no chance whatsoever that he was going to build an empire and make his descendants fat cats on the inheritance. But I don't think he was as bad as his neighbour, Dunlea, made out. Dunlea quoted Murphy as saying, "well isn't that a grand wet day, thank God." Ah no, he wasn't that bad, he didn't pray for the elements to relieve him from his toil, he merely saw the silver lining in the dark clouds.

"Murphy's a quare hawk," Dunlea would say with a grin. I was only six, so I had no idea what he meant. Many years later it was clearer to me that Murphy's easy going style, his funny turn of phrase, that he sometimes served Mass in a little country chapel when he was sixty years of age, and that he knew nearly as much latin as a priest, made him in Dunlea's eyes, "a quare hawk." His home place isn't on the map, but it does have a school and a church, and Murphy's house was wedged in between the two of them.

My first real memories of Murphy start when I was about five and he was about sixty. He never wore glasses, which belies the belief that reading in poor light makes one blind. Electricity hadn't yet come to the area, so he read with the aid of a big oil lamp with two wicks and a large glass globe, which stood in the centre of the table in the big kitchen. He carried a big pocket watch, with a long chain, and wore a hat that was always tilted towards the back of his head. The war was over, Hitler was defeated and Europe was getting off its knees. Murphy was interested in events, so on about two nights a week he visited Kennedy who lived just a few long strides down the road. There he could hear the news and test his knowledge with Joe Linnane's "Question Time". Kennedy had the wireless and Murphy had the curiosity. Oh yes, and if he could make it around to Palmer, on the back road, there might even be a game of cards.

When I started school reading and writing weren't quite foreign to me. You see I used to follow Murphy almost every day and he was generous with the information, and like him with news, I was curious. On the bog, or in a field far from the house, he would have sandwiches. Some for me of course also, and always wrapped in newspaper. I don't think Mrs

Murphy worried too much about printing ink from the newspaper getting on the bread. Anyhow, when the dining was over the learning began. He would read from the paper that wrapped the sandwiches, and having set a good example he would get me to have a go. Later back in the house he'd give me a short pencil and he'd try to retrieve from my head the knowledge he had imparted in the hedge school.

In spite of his easy going ways, Murphy was no softie. He would never have taken to electric blankets, had they been around in his time. In the depths of winter I saw him go around to the water barrel that stood at the end of the house, smash the ice, dip his pair of big hands and splash the freezing water on his face. It used to give me the shivers just looking at him. Mrs Murphy didn't approve either, early in the morning she would tie-up her long hair and sip warm water before breakfast.

Kennedy used to cut Murphy's hair and the sound of the scissors was enough to send me flying. I hated having my hair cut, but Murphy always insisted on the double header. Kennedy needed practice, so I was captured in the cow shed, hauled in and clipped. It was the only time I disliked Murphy. Though in fairness to him, at other times he'd make up for having surrendered me to the mercy of Kennedy. Mrs Murphy sometimes saw fit to chase me for some minor indiscretion or other and Murphy would impede her progress and aid my escape.

He hated pills of any kind, and doctors might as well be statues for all the attention he paid to them. Whenever he got minor afflictions he took himself off to St. Fintan's Well, which lay a few miles distant. He'd drink liberally from the well, mumble a few prayers, mount his horse, with me up behind him, and ride home with his health on the mend. I can't ever recall him spending a day sick in bed. Sometimes Dunlea would call for him early in the morning, expecting him to be in bed, as he most likely was. "Is your grandfather not up yet?" he'd ask. "Get him out of it," he'd order me, shouting after me as I went, "Murphy's a quare hawk."

— O —

Murphy at 81.

A Railway Station of yesterday. (Courtesy of Leabharlann Naisiunta na hEireann).

A Deserted Railway Station

THE little railway station was empty and deserted, weeds peeped between the paving slabs that covered the platform. The doorway that led to the waiting room and ticket office was bricked up. It was many years since the last train pulled out, and standing there in a light drizzle on a late summer evening, I wondered about the last passenger to buy a ticket here and where he may have travelled to. It was here I first saw a train, and from this station I made my first train journey. The station carried the name of the town that lies a few miles distant, Mountrath, but was known locally by the townland it stood in, Kilbricken. A stones-throw from the station there was, and still is, a pub. It was often the hurdle that a traveller failed to make, and a seat on the train that should have been warm went ice cold to Dublin.

It was a busy place back then, supplies for the surrounding area came by rail and were delivered by lorries. My sweetest memories of the little railway station is of big match days and the excursion train. The wearers of the blue and white didn't often give us the thrill of the victor's cup but, nevertheless, we travelled in hope. While the homecoming might be one of downcast eyes and heavy heart, the outward-bound was always full of bright expectation. Dinny Walsh and myself would leave our bicycles in Glennon's hayshed and take the shortcut across the field and down the railway line to the station. The little platform might be full, for it didn't take many to fill it. "The signal's down" someone would say, and all heads would look up the tracks to confirm that the arm had dropped and the light was green, the train had left Ballybrophy. We stood there like Indians from the old west, waiting for the iron horse. The railway-line was straight as a laser beam, and it seemed to narrow as it faded in the distance beyond vision's range. And out of this nothingness appeared a black speck that grew until we could see the pot bellied shape and the long funnel. The modern diesel is no match in spectacle for the steam engine. A sharp blast on the whistle was warning to keep back, then the train slid into the station, the driving mechanism of its wheels visible, and moving with the precision of a clock. Belching steam around the ankles of the waiting passengers it would grind to a halt.

From his open backed engine the driver leaning over the side exchanged chat with the people on the platform, while his helper opened the furnace door to feed more coal to what looked like the fires of hell. And that smell of burning fuel peculiar to steam trains, a sort of railway perfume, it would linger in the traveller's nostrils long after the journey was completed. Then we were moving, the chug, chug, sound of the engine, black puffs of smoke drifting across the countryside like little clouds and the clickity click of the wheels, the build up of speed until the train swayed like a drunkard walking a corridor.

It all came to mind as I stood on the platform remembering how it used to be. Concrete blocks filled the frame of the old doorway to the waitingroom. There was no getting in to see if the walls were still green and if the bench seat was still there, and perhaps even a few posters, extolling the virtues of travel by rail. I wondered if the ticket hatch still existed, that sliding shutter through which the little piece of cardboard came, the ticket to ride. Beyond the platform, lying among the grass and weeds, was a twisted heap of steel. It used to be the footbridge for crossing the tracks. The glass fronted signal cabin with its rows of well oiled levers was no more. The man who sat here controlled the movement of every train within his sector. Roses used to grow around the cabin, only its foundation remains now, but the roses still grow, blooming like some kind of memorial to a time that used to be. The line is now controlled from many miles away by a small box of electronic gadgetry. No more friendly waves from the signal man, no chat from the driver of an open backed engine.

As darkness fell the deserted station was quiet. The lamp standards along the platform still stand but no light came from them. It was raining lightly as I stood there with an umbrella over my head, remembering the place as it used to be. At that moment a train passed through the station, and it may well be that some passenger on that train is telling a story about seeing a ghost standing on the platform of a deserted station between Portlaoise and Ballybrophy. Such a thought may not be too far wrong, for as I stood there I was aware of a traveller from long ago waiting for another train.

— 0 —

Childhood Hero

EVERY now and then someone is plucked from among us and elevated to the plain of adulation, and some spend all their lives there simply because of an accident of birth. The yardstick of this greatness is indeed a very fallible thing. The faces that stare at me daily from the newspapers have the opposite effect to that desired by the starer. The gods of commerce and politics and so on, perpetually fill me with disappointment. I don't want to be a soldier in this man's army.

If one is looking for a real hero, there's not much around. So back I wander to childhood days and there is no veneer covering my hero. My young eyes were not deceived, for I look back and I remember Paddy Kennedy, and I feel a glow of satisfaction. He was not a man who took life too seriously, he appealed to the young perhaps greater than to his own peers.

Paddy Kennedy is long gone and there's no need to rack your brain trying to establish who he was, I doubt he was ever known much beyond the boundaries of his own parish. He lived at the top of the hill two hundred yards from my grandfather's house. Paddy ran a small farm and his house was of the picture postcard type, with whitewashed walls and flowers everywhere. The hedges were trimmed into the shapes of birds and animals, and other shapes that represented nothing, abstract art from his head, expressed through a hedge.

It wasn't his gift with a hedge clipper that endeared him to me. He did nothing that was noted outside the parish, yet everything he did, if done on a grander scale, might have immortalised him. It was a time when a young lad had little say, kids were very definitely seen and not heard — it sometimes seemed they were intended not to be seen too often either — but Paddy listened, and he talked, and he explained, and above all he seemed to understand. He had a habit of getting up early in the morning, and so had I, and it was a habit of mine to call on him equally early.

I'd look up the hill and if a wisp of smoke came from the chimney I'd know Paddy was up and cooking breakfast over his open turf fire. In I'd go and join him and share his fry, and there never was a time when I didn't feel welcome.

He took me to the fields in the evenings and taught me how to set snares for rabbits. Sitting on the haycart with him he'd give me the reins and let me drive, and once he was foolish enough — after much persuasion from me — to hand me control of a plough. I zigzagged all over the place and he didn't take it back from me until the plough leaped out of the ground, and even then he blamed it on the horse saying, "that ould horse won't work right for anyone but meself."

It was a time in rural Ireland when ready-made entertainment was very scarce. Visiting each other, telling stories and the odd practical joke helped to inject a little life and laughter into what was otherwise very spartan lives. Paddy Kennedy kept himself occupied and entertained and in the process did likewise for his neighbours, even if at times it was neither understood nor appreciated. Such as the rainy day standing at the graveside of a young mother, when the officiating priest — a most pompous man — slipped on the wet clay and almost fell into the grave. Paddy laughed, and did so out loud at that. Nobody seemed amused, least of all the pompous cleric, but no-one there could have felt more sorrow for the family than Paddy. In the days and months to follow, it was he, more than anyone else who brought moments of consolation to that woman's husband and children. He could mingle the tear with the smile, and yet know where each belonged.

The swallows built their nests under the eaves of his house and it was always a fascination to me watching the activity during nesting time. One autumn day when they were all lined up along a clothes line in front of his house and I asked him for an explanation, he went inside and brought out an old, tattered atlas, "they're off to Africa for the winter," he said, using the atlas to show me where, and how far away it was, and adding, "maybe some day you'll go there too."

To me then, Africa wasn't just another continent, it was another planet, and little did I know that one day I would indeed follow the swallows.

Many years passed before I again visited Shanahoe. Driving up to Paddy Kennedy's house I noticed the hedges weren't as trim as before, and the paint on the old green gate was weather worn and flaking. Fearing the worst, I walked into the yard and along by the rose garden. There he was, hoe in hand, tending his flowers. Knowing that he had last seen me as a teenager, I spoke but didn't identify myself. There wasn't much chance for any planned deception, he uttered my name before I had time to wonder. In the little kitchen of his house we spent two hours covering twenty years and he was to me that evening, as a man, everything he had been to me as a child. We parted with many promises of get-togethers soon again, but they were never to be, he died within a few months.

The following summer, passing through Shanahoe, I paused outside Paddy's house. It was closed, and the walls were no longer white, no inviting smoke from the chimney, no life, other than the swallows, who like myself came back from Africa. The roses had gone wild and choked themselves, and the hedges, although still there, had buried the art work through many years of unchecked growth. It would be nice to find a hero for grown men to match the man that Paddy Kennedy was.

School Days

MY memories of school days are very mixed. They had, of course, the odd rosy patch, but equally, they were never without the thorns. I was about six when Martin Breen was building the new school across the road from our house. Somewhere deep in the concrete there are several small footprints. He had just finished laying the fresh concrete when I paraded down the middle, pausing only to admire the marks I was making. For my sins I was tied to the school gate. The punishment worked, I never again walked on Breen's concrete.

I was living with my grandparents at that time, and in large fields just beyond the tiny hamlet, I remember seeing big wooden stakes all over the place. The teacher, Mrs O'Connell, was a mine of information, so I asked her about the stakes. "They were put there to prevent German war planes from landing," she said. The war was now long over, but she said that there had been many such staked fields. This information fascinated me, so I sought more from Paddy Kennedy. He said the story was correct, and that when Hitler heard about it he said "They shouldn't bother, that if he was coming it wouldn't be in his bare feet."

The second school I attended was about six miles away. It might as well have been in China. I don't think I ever fully forgot the trauma of the change. My grandparents were now getting on, and I had to return to my parents. But for many years to come I would look back and think of the old place as home. The new school took a lot of getting used to. Mrs O'Connell was a normal sort of human being, and she was great at answering questions, but now this new teacher didn't seem to like being asked questions at all. He was a De La Salle brother, and his long black cassock had an unsettling effect on me. If chalk kills one he must have died young, for he was never without a piece dangling from a corner of his mouth. There are memories of cold winter mornings and a line of about six lads out by the wall, and the brother going along the line with his sally rod, administering punishment for things that were then beyond our understanding. He'd say, "You can't make a silk purse out of a sows ear." The pity was he never heard the echo of what he was saying. I more or less escaped that firing squad, but at music I got the full salvo. I simply could not distinguish between sounds, and for that I had the tuning fork tested on my head.

Eamon was the nearest thing to a loveable rogue that I can think of. He

17

was funny, full of devilment, and as unpredicatable as an Irish summer. He fell in for his share of the firing squad, but he never flinched. He'd tighten his mouth and narrow his eyes, as if to say, 'do your worst, but I won't cry'. He held the mitching record for the school, and God knows, who would blame him, seeing what he often had to face. On several occasions the teacher formed a posse from the rest of us, and led us into the nearby woods to search for Eamon. In this, Eamon had a weakness, he always hid in the same place. One such morning we found him inside the hollowed out stump of a tree. We pretended not to see him, this extended the search until the teacher spotted him. Back to the school we marched, the teacher with Eamon by the ear. At the school Eamon opened the gate for the teacher, stepped through and promptly slammed it and escaped again. Such events broke the monotony of dull days.

It was years later that I envied the children who were lucky enough to have been pupils of Brian McMahon and his like. There was so much around us to marvel at and have explained to us. Right by the school we had a lovely river, full with salmon and trout. We had a waterfall, a castle and a mill. A few miles out the road we worked with our parents in bogs that surrendered to us the remnants of trees that were millions of years old. Facing our school was the mountain, a mountain that was snow capped when the valley was still green. On its slopes, some of the finest woods in Ireland. A place to ease a burdened mind, while marvelling at the surrounding beauty. All of this around us and no one with the soul or vision to explain it to us. And from that school the lads left for the coalmines and the building sites of England. They left without a legacy of nature, a legacy that might have befriended them on dark days.

For me, early school days were just blackboards and chalk, bare wooden floors, and ink stained desks. The map on the wall was like the torch in the hand of the statue of liberty, a symbol of hope. We had little awareness then of places beyond the range of our vision. But that map seemed to pull back a curtain on another world, a world that some of us would one day see.

— o —

Joe the Post

IT was early morning in a country village and I was watching a little van driving from house to house. It took me a while to realise it was the postman, it was the van that confused me. The last postman I saw delivering mail in that village had a big green post office bike and he was as much a part of the life of the community as was the church where they prayed.

There's a hint of magic and mystery about a postman. He may well bring you the good the bad and the ugly, but memory being selective it tends to recall only the letters that brought the good news. When Joe, our postman, pedalled the roads and boreens of our neighbourhood it was a time when letters meant more that they do today. Only a handful of people had telephones, and when the youngsters left the nest of home for far flung places it was through the written word that contact was maintained.

He was a small man, and as well as the mailbag on his back he carried parcels on the carrier in front of the bicycle. Often as he pedalled away from the post office in the mornings he could barely be seen behind the sack of mail in front of him. I'd meet him in the village and he'd say "I have nothing with your photo on it today." He brought newspapers to people who lived far from the village, as well as the odd small item that would save them a trip to town. Give him a letter and he'd stamp it and mail it for you in the village.

The local disco of the day was the village hall, with Joe and his brother supplying the music. A pair of short, craggy faced men, sitting on stools playing accordions. And like Henry Ford's motor cars of the day, where you could have any colour as long as it was black, with Joe and the brother you could have any tune as long as it was an old-time waltz. It was here that all us youngsters of the village had our introduction to the dance-floor before we ventured to the dizzy heights of the ballroom in the town.

Modern clocks and watches are accurate to within a fraction of a second, a small piece of quartz guaranteering the precision. Our postman never heard of quartz in a watch, but he took out springs and cogs and reassembled them and hundreds of clocks and watches that had gone silent were once again ticking away on mantlepieces, in pockets and on wrists.

I have visions of Joe on wet days and he covered from head to toe in black oilskins. His hat like that worn by fishermen and the rain running off it like the eve of a house, some of it dripping into the mailbag causing the ink on the envelopes to run a bit. He tended to whistle as he cycled along, a sound as distinct as the curlews that swooped over the bog. There were many of them, but there was only one whistling postman and it brought people from behind ditches and walls in anticipation of a piece of mail.

In an age of poor communications and difficult travel he was the daily newsletter of the parish. He brought news of the condition of a neighbour who was ill, or news of who was home on holidays, or more likely in those days, who was the latest departure to join McAlpines troops in England. He was often the web of communication that united the extremities of a scattered rural population. Right down to the unwelcome mail Joe designed his own soft landings. Bills were identifiable, but he never called them bills. As he handed you one and you voiced your disgust, he'd say, "don't look at it that way, it's only a letter with a window."

Every Christmas Eve Joe had a pattern that was as precise as the clocks he repaired. He was on the road before sunrise and it was long after sunset when he got back to the village. All those people for whom he had rendered such service during the year now pressed the compliments of the season on him, and the last mile home on that bike was an unsteady one. But by midnight he was all dressed up and back to sing in the choir. Joe the Post was a once off. Postman, musician, watchmaker, gentleman.

— O —

John Keegan

FOLLOWERS of a village team are often passionate in their support. Even at an All-Ireland the same degree of fervour isn't there, it's just the big crowd that makes it feel more vibrant. It's all to do with the sense of identification, you a part of them and they a part of you. Shanahoe, in the heart of Co. Laois, isn't even a village, but it did give us John Keegan. It's perhaps not surprising if you never heard of him. It was a long time ago, and he was not of the stature of the greats.

It's nice to go along and see the places associated with Shaw and Joyce and O'Casey and so on, but for me the land of John Keegan is home ground, it's that village team. I was very young in that old schoolhouse in Shanahoe when Mrs O'Connell told me about John Keegan. "He taught here", she said, "and he lived in Killeaney, down past the water pump and over the hill". To me then anywhere over that hill was far away and I could feel the tiredness that must have been upon him as he walked to school. Mrs O'Connell read one of his poems and I was fascinated by the imagery it conjured up. It was the story of a blind piper, Caoch O'Leary and his dog "Pinch".

"One Winter's day, long, long ago,
when I was a little fellow.
A piper wandered to our door,
grey headed, blind and yellow.
And, oh, how glad was my young heart,
though earth and sky looked dreary.
To see the stranger and his dog
poor "Pinch" and Caoch O'Leary."

So goes the first verse. There are greater poems than "Caoch the Piper" and better poets than John Keegan, but there are no threads to connect me to them. Whereas with Keegan I sat for several seasons of my youth within the same walls as he once did and every day I walked the same roads. Within an asse's roar of Shanahoe you find little places of local legend about which he wrote. His story "The Baccough Ruadh" is still passed on in the area. It tells the tale of a one legged, red headed beggar, who made a fortune sitting by the river at a point where it was forded by stepping stones. The legend lives on and the bridge that now spans the river Nore between Shanahoe and Abbeyleix is known as "Poor Man's Bridge".

It's a story of a little joy and a lot of sorrow, much as was Keegan's own life. Born in 1809, he died in Dublin of cholera when he was forty. His marriage failed and his daughter died young. His own death almost went unnoticed, it was unreported for a fortnight. Cholera was rampant at the time and it seems he may have been buried on the same day that he died. The newspaper "The Irishman" on the 14th of July 1849 published a tribute. In part it said, "He was a poor man, he had no property but his intellect. In our time that is a miserable patrimony. Poetry is surplus and the demand does not equal the supply. His poems were thoroughly and racy of the soil. They touched us more than the polished lines of drawingroom bards. Because they did not consecrate affectation, but showed us ourselves."

A series of his short stories appeared in the "Dublin University Magazine", but most of his work was for "Dolman's Magazine". At various times he contributed to "The Nation" and "The Irishman", the latter publishing some of his best poems.

In an introduction to his stories he described himself. "I am an Irish peasant, born and reared in an Irish cabin and educated in an Irish hedge-school. I have spent my years among the lower classes of the insulted and despised Irish peasantry. On Sundays I have knelt with them before the same wide altar, on weekdays I have wrought with them in the same fields." Little did he know that one hundred and fifty years later someone would walk the same fields and roads and remember him and be grateful for the legacy he left. His house is long gone and cattle now graze the lush grass where it once stood beside the river Gully in the shadow of Gortnacle Castle.

Shanahoe is still much as it was in Keegan's day. They had a band back then and Keegan played the trombone in it. Today, the little hamlet is silent to the sound of music. But on the green hill beyond it isn't hard to imagine the sound of Keegan's trombone echoing across the valley to join with the pipes of Caoch O'Leary. For he may have been sitting on that same hill on a Summer evening watching the shadows creeping across Shanahoe when he wrote:

"The red sun poured its evening beam
On lowland tower and lowland stream.
And earth was green and heaven was blue,
For Summer wore its richest hue."

I've read most of what he wrote and it all comes back to Mrs O'Connell in the old schoolhouse and that very first poem. I can see this old man knocking at our door, his bagpipes under his arm and his dog standing beside him, as weary as his master. Like the village team, it's simply a sense of identification.

The Village

PEOPLE have always talked about the 'good old days'. Quite likely when Saint Patrick returned to convert the Irish he said the same about his days herding sheep in the Antrim Hills. Quite possibly a hundred years from now they'll be referring to the good old days of the 1990's, when they had pollution and nuclear threats and no jobs.

There's little to be said for the good old days, in fact they were mostly very bad old days. Memory tends to be selective and to go for the soft option; to hold onto the good bits and bury the bad ones. Now, without getting into a discourse on whether or not things were better yesterday, I feel that most periods in time, are, on balance, better than a time before.

Thoughts of this nature came to mind recently when spending a couple of hours walking by the river near my home village. It's a place well known to me — all my days were spent there until I was nineteen. A quiet place, set in good farming country. It has today, as it had in my childhood, a few shops, a post office, a pub, a church, and a boys and girls school. It still puzzles me to find one good reason why the handful of boys and girls have to go to different schools. The Dublin-Limerick road ran through the village until a bypass was built some years ago. Today the village is quiet, while the juggernauts roar by a few hundred yards away. Still standing, sentry like, in the middle of the village, is the old wooden water pump. For generations it was the sole source of water supply, until about twenty years ago, when piped water was laid on.

The green triangle at the bottom of the village, where we played hurling every spare hour of our young lives, is a quiet, sedate place now. No more the echo of the clash of the ash, or the anxious yells of young voices doing reckless damage to shins as they scurried in pursuit of a small leather ball. The green triangle is still there, but tall trees now grow on our hurling field, and park benches and rose bushes suggest a more leisurely generation.

That's the village, and definitely it's better today than when I lived there. In fact in recent years it won several major prizes in the Tidy Towns competition. Right below the village runs the river Nore. The river is deep and wide when it reaches Castletown, having filled itself well as it came thundering down the Sliabh Bloom mountains. This river was a focal point of our youth. It was ever present, for even at night as we lay in our beds we could clearly hear the steady noise of the water splashing over the weir. The only time it went silent was when several days of heavy rain sent the brown water tumbling down from the mountain, filling the river over its banks and covering the waterfall.

I stood on the bridge recently, I looked at the old mill, it's silent now. The water still passes through, but the big wheel is gone. Along the top of the bridge wall a little moss grows, the stones used to be smooth and shiny from backsides and hands. In winter, apart from us locals, people passing through would stop on the bridge to see the salmon. The weir is just below the bridge, and there you could see the salmon jumping against the water, as they tried to make their way up-river to spawn. There's a little stairway of falls there now and the salmon don't need to be fit anymore to jump past Castletown. Good for them, but what a spectacle we lost.

Just beyond the old bridge was a deep part of the river we called the swimming pool. I learned to swim there, as did all the neighbourhood. A big tree hung in across the swimming pool, we made one large branch extra smooth and used it as a diving board. We sat in old motor tubes and let the current take us down-river until it dumped us over the falls. The diving tree is gone and in its place is the concrete support of the new bridge that carries the by-pass, that carries the juggernauts.

There was an abundance of hazel growing along its banks, and it was nice to see that a lot of it is still there. We collected sacks of nuts from those trees. Further up there was a little wood, it was a wonderland in summer. Sitting there and watching the waterhens dashing to and fro on the river, to the background sound of cooing pigeons in the wood. It was a great place for wild flowers and I recall the profusion of colour and the scented air, the smooth velvety feel of the dark green moss. It wasn't a big wood, very small really, but it was a world within a world. It's all gone now, no trees, no flowers, no moss, just a nice flat piece of arable land. I suppose the waterhens have moved on to a place with greater cover.

That stretch of river was definitely better then. But all is not lost, the village is a bigger, better and brighter place than it ever was before. The kids of today don't have a tree for a diving board, the new bridge crosses right over the swimming pools. So instead they have a roof. Maybe they will look back and say that they had an indoor pool. One other thing that hasn't changed, I can still go to sleep in my mother's house to the music of the water cascading over the falls.

— O —

24

The Nore at Castletown.

Reaper and Binder cutting oats. (Courtesy of Bord Fáilte).

Yesterday's Farmer

PERHAPS it's not an exaggeration to say that very soon no-one will know how to count, that is without the aid of a calculator. Progress is an ill-defined word. I'm thinking now in particular in relation to farming. When the first tractors came to Ireland there must have been many a farmer who dropped on his knees in the middle of a field and thanked God for deliverance. In the main technology has made modern farming easier and more effective. There is of course a dark side to it as well. Cattle today are on a perpetual high, if they were humans they'd all be in some detoxification centre. As for some vegetables, well you'd need no insect killer while you'd have them in the house.

There's an era dead and gone that's well worth remembering. When I was a teenager the two ages were living side by side. The new had arrived but the old was still gold to that other generation. I'm glad to have experienced the last days of that other era.

The combine harvester replaced the reaper and binder, it was indeed aptly named — reaper and binder. I could watch that old machine in operation with the same enthusiasm that another might display while listening to Yehudi Menuhin playing the violin. It was magic to my eyes and ears. You started with a field of golden corn and usually a sunny day. Then as the blades severed the corn it fell back gently onto the rolling canvas. It was taken upwards through two other canvasses and into a bay to form a sheaf. An ingenious mechanism brought the twine around it, tied it and cut it. Then two metal rods did a twirl and spat the sheaf out. It was collected by hand and made into small stacks and the rough edges on the ears of corn made the insides of your bare arms go red.

The modern tractor ploughs at a pace and the whole field seems to be turning over at once, and there's the noise of the engine and the smell of diesel. As a lad I followed behind Murphy and the two horses and the sounds we heard came from the harness as it strained and the plough as it sliced the earth and our eyes caught the green as it turned to brown as the earth rolled over. And overhead crows hovered like little black helicopters, cawing anxiously, as if to hurry us along, to turn more earth and reveal more food.

Warm summer days and haymaking go together. Today the baler does the work, it spews out heavy, tightly pressed bales, like giant concrete blocks. We threw up the loose stuff by hand and made haycocks with nice rounded tops, so that the rain ran off. There was always an urgency to beat the weather and the tea was brought to the field and currant cake came with it, as a sort of compensation for the extra effort. The sweat ran down and burned your eyes, and maybe the sun burned your back through a hole in your shirt. But we had craic among ourselves, while the River Nore flowed dark and silent beside us. And the perfumed hay, ah, if you could bottle that fragrance, and the rhythmic clanging of a mowing machine in a distant field and the distinctive sound of a corncrake protesting at the disturbance.

Nowadays you can get a free digital watch with a tank of petrol. Back then young lads rarely had watches, and the ones owned by the elders didn't seem to keep very good time. No one ever asked 'do you have the time?'' It was always, 'do you have the right time?'' If we were without a watch we did like the Indian scouts, we used the sights and sounds around us to indicate the hour. A passing train, shadows, animal movements, the angelus bell from a distant church faintly reaching our ears, high noon, or six in the evening and time to close the day.

Today's farmer down by the River Nore not alone has a timepiece, but he has a built-in stopwatch so he can check the precision of his machines. The back-breaking labour is gone, but bigger unfortunately doesn't mean better. Today we have butter mountains and beef mountains and grain mountains. We have farmers getting heart attacks trying to get their produce onto any mountain. When I was a kid we had no mountains, not even little hills, and of course we had very few heart attacks.

It seems to have gone too far too fast, nature has been bent to suit the altar of profit. That is most likely our biggest mistake, for while nature will ever be your partner, she will never be your slave. What has been taken will have to be given back. Drugged animals, chemically damaged soil and polluted rivers will have to be redressed. If we don't start the healing process now, generations to come will curse us for the legacy we left them. In the meantime I'll dream of distant summer days and the smell of new mown hay. Patrick Kavanagh once wrote, "Oh stony grey soil of Monaghan you burgled my bank of youth." I would say of the fields of Laois, you often broke my back, but you put a deposit in my bank of youth from which today I am drawing the biggest dividends I ever did.

— o —

Teenage Friends

THE social life of my little village in the late 1950's would never make the national gossip columns. In fact it was a claim to fame if you got your name in the 'local notes' of the 'Leinster Express'. I never made such dizzy heights, my only ego booster was to see my name handwritten on a page torn from a school jotter, indicating that I was a substitute on the local hurling team. This was on prominent display in Dunne's shop window.

There was no television then, in fact not everyone had a radio. Discos were still twenty years away and the principal means of transport — a bike — kept a lad very fit and often very, very wet.

Work was hard and long and despite what some might think today, it was much scarcer then. The pay was bad — even the best of it. That was the setting against which we lived our teenage years.

We felt things deeply, but we didn't understand them. The social deprivations of that period was an accepted fact. We knew of a finer order of things beyond but not quite how to attain it. Like dogs that huddle together on a bitter cold night, we pals stuck together as if the world we sought might be reached through power of numbers.

Doadie was my best friend. We had discovered common ground from an early age. Together we planned our attack on life and dreamt our dreams of that world beyond.

He was allowed to the pictures when I wasn't, but the following evening, sitting on the river bank, he would tell me the whole story and you know, some of them I can remember better than many a good film I was later to see myself. We swopped every experience and delighted in making comparisons of the ones we had both been through.

At school we sat together and spent many an hour playing a game of our own concoction, where each in turn would find a place on the large map of the world which hung on the wall beside us, then tell the place-name to the other and let him go find it. I knew many a city all over the world long before I had the correct pronunciation of its name.

I had other pals of course, but Doadie was the king, he was smart, he knew things the other lads didn't and he always had an opinion on anything you asked him.

Can you imagine the trauma and disaster for me the day he got a job in Dublin. That evening, when he told me, if someone had amputated my two legs I doubt I could have felt worse. For weeks I went around like a hen in a desert, until I began to spread my wings marginally and seek through the rest of the bunch, some of the outlets I had lost. It was the first of many such losses, where circumstances swept friends away, only I had started at the top.

Chris was seventeen, blond, knew great jokes and had a multi-geared bike. We wore out many tyres and suffered many a fall while trying to beat him in races around the village green. One Sunday evening the Parish Priest came out and we were petrified he was going to ban our regular afternoon 'Tour de France'. To our amazement and delight he offered a half crown — and that was a fortune then — for that evening's winner.

Chris was leading by a street and out to impress the Parish Priest by really hareing it round the bends until he skidded on loose gravel, leaving myself and a chap named Phelan to dead-heat and split the half crown. It was shortly after that that Chris got a girlfriend and almost over-night we as good as lost him completely. It was again a traumatic period, but not as bad as before. We spent months trying to convince Chris to give up the girlfriend, but to no avail. In fact she eventually became his wife.

The lads who were exceptionally good at hurling stood apart. They might be classed as 'hero type' pals. They got their names in the paper regularly and sometimes, their pictures. There was status attached to being in their company. Then, one by one, like the others, they were off to London. I developed a dislike for that city, it was constantly gobbling up my friends.

Larry and I hunted rabbits and climbed tall trees after bird's nests and he told me the first joke I ever heard that might be classified as a dirty one — at least then it would. He had a great feeling for dogs and he knew much about wild birds and fish. He could find nuts and wild berries as if he had a detecting device in his head.

There never was much build-up to these things, they always seemed to come out of the blue. His brother Pat was home on holidays from England and he would be going back with him.

The chain kept breaking, every now and then someone else was lost to some foreign city. We were ageing and adjusting, the process of growing up and fanning out was alive amongst us. We didn't recognise it and felt it mostly as a series of painful losses.

Then one day my call came, with my bike and suitcase on top of the bus I was only looking ahead. I wonder did anyone feel lonely that evening?

— o —

30

The Turfmen

THE annual ritual of winning the winter's fire still goes on, that time when men, and some women, go down to the bogs. For a while it was a dying practice, but it seems to be picking up again. The use of the bogs is to an extent determined by the cost of alternative fuels. A few more disasters, such as the tanker that spilled millions of gallons of oil near Alaska, or the oil rigs that toppled in the North Sea, then we'd all be getting out the maps searching for areas marked 'boglands'. When we'd get there some of us would be more equal than others. For many it would be a sort of reincarnation, a life we had lived before.

At worst it was back-breaking work that lasted a week and demanded as much preparation as a Moslem making a trip to Mecca. When the week was over you were sore in places you never knew you had muscles. But there was a sweet side to it as well. A sod of turf isn't a work of art, but it takes neat skill to cut one. On our bog the tool used for cutting was called a slane, elsewhere they pronounced it slán. However, slane or slán, it sliced through the wet turf. A twist of the wrist broke it off, and in one clean movement the slane propelled the sod from the boghole and straight into the hands of a waiting catcher. A practised and skilled movement, as satisfying to the man making it, as for a golfer who lands a two-hundred yard drive beside the pin.

There was very much an established hierarchy among the turf cutting crew. The man using the slane was quite definitely Mr. Big. In descending order they went down through catchers and barrow pushers to the young lads who made the tea. Now tea at a table is one thing, but tea on the bog is something else. As soon as you arrived at the work-site a fire was lit. A bunch of dried heather and an armful of twigs and soon the smoke was rising to the heavens. And from high ground overlooking the bog thirty such fires could be seen. A forked stick pushed into the ground on either side of the fire and another piece of wood resting across them, it supported a black kettle that bubbled and boiled merrily. The tea was coming, God was in his heaven and all was well with the world.

Milk didn't come in cartons then, in fact in rural areas it didn't even come in bottles. It was milked by hand and the first jet of milk rang against the bottom of the tin bucket like a bullet against a galvanised roof. It was often brought to the bog in a whiskey bottle, with rolled newspaper for a stopper. The bottle was pushed into the soft wet turf until only the neck stuck up, and there it stayed, cool and as fresh as if in a four star fridge.

There must be something in us which keeps pulling us back towards our origins. Back to the time ages ago when man lit fires with flints and sat around them in the open, cooking his catch of wild animals and birds. Otherwise how can you explain the absolute pleasure of making a fire from the scatterings of nature. Then cooking a meal on it and eating it sitting on soft turf in the middle of a bog. Tea made from water boiled in a black kettle and sausages fried on an equally black pan, and both of them tasting of smoke.

As the day wore on and the boghole got deeper and the rows of newly cut black turf stretched further away, about that time a visitor would call. He was a man who would walk the bog from end to end, calling in on everyone who worked there. Today he would be working in management consultancy, comparing the efficiency or otherwise of one company with another. Our man never saw the outside of a company never mind the inside. But he stood there, hands deep in his pockets delivering progress reports on our neighbours up and down the line. He inspected our work and he criticised and he praised, and as Albert, who worked beside us said "he wouldn't know a good job from the side of a mountain."

The going down of the sun brought blessed relief. The coats, that rested all day on the heather, now covered aching backs. The tools were hidden in a drain until the next morning. The last train to Dublin passed across the scene like a comet. From all directions small groups made their way along the narrow road that led from the bog to their homes. In the winter nights ahead they would smoke their pipes and draw warmth and satisfaction from the glowing turf.

— o —

The Castle Ballroom

DANCING — that is real dancing — is excellent for exercise. It has a few other advantages which I would venture to say would take priority over the exercise aspect, like, for example, meeting fellow fitness fiends, of the opposite sex of course. Nowadays, with social activities greatly expanded, the dancehall is just one other place where boy may meet girl, but twenty five years ago in rural Ireland, it was the only place where boy might meet girl.

The Castle Ballroom in Mountrath was castle only in name. It boasted no turrets, nor lofty hall, nor did the sound of music climb the steps of a graceful stairway. Tin walls and tin roof — commonly known as galvanise then — painted green, and even the window glass was also painted. Sparse and basic, it was here that my friend, Andy, and myself made our debut in ballroom dancing as a pair of seventeen year olds. It's so easy now to look back and laugh and find it all so amusing. But when you've never heard of the Metropole or the Lyceum, then the Castle Ballroom in Mountrath is 'cock of the walk'.

It's all so much easier today. A lad gets on the floor with his girl, stands facing her with three or four feet of clearance, he shifts his weight from left foot to right foot to left foot, and maintains that rhythm until it's time to go. The din is usually so great that conversation is out. No such luck back then in the Castle Ballroom. That little band of part-time musicians that were also part-time farmers and part-time shop assistants and part-time lorry drivers, and possibly because they were part-time everything, they played softly, which meant you could talk to your partner, and you would be heard. Therefore you needed something sensible to say. But that was the advanced section, first off you had to ask someone to dance, and the first problem was how to hold her, even where to hold her. Looking at what the other fellow was doing wasn't much help. It was a bit like looking in a mirror, wondering which was left and which was right, more confusing than helpful. And all of that was only the beginning.

Next came the requirement for some knowledge of foxtrots, quicksteps, tangos and sambas. No wonder Andy and I asked up for our first dance two girls whose mothers were friends of our mothers. It was a strategy of a kind. They were somewhat experienced, and being daughters of friendly mothers, were less likely to reject us. My girl's name was Lil, and God bless her tolerance, for I stood on everything except the floor, but mainly on her feet, and she bore it all for the mammy's sake. And the part-time band played some real slow and soft numbers and there was great space for conversation, if only I had time. But I was too busy thinking about how I should hold Lil, and at the same time trying to keep my feet out of her way.

'Time', it is said, 'heals all wounds', and no doubt it healed Lil's feet. The quicksteps and the foxtrots and the lot were mastered sufficiently to allow Andy and myself to venture beyond the mammies' friends. Very soon Sunday nights in the Castle became a regular event for us. The bumpy floor became a challenge — trying to avoid the bad bits. And the mineral bar, that served just that, lemonade or orange, in the bottle, no glass, no straw, but it tasted great. No wonder we needed drinks, especially the lads, with odds of about two to one in the ladies' favour. To get an even break you'd need to dance like Fred Astaire and look like Omar Sharif — as they were then of course — all of which stretched the odds against Andy and me further still.

Christmas was always much better in the Castle. Apart from the few balloons and streamers that broke the monotony of the tin walls and tin roof, there was the return of the emigrants. They were mostly females, and this put a little equilibrium into things for a few weeks. For the rest of the year the high point of the night was when the band would stop — mid-tune — and announce "two tickets for next Sunday night to the first person up with a bicycle pump," and suddenly half the people in the hall were on the stage. Or the night the two tickets went unclaimed, when the reward was offered to "the first man up without a hole in his socks." And talking of rewards, there should certainly have been one for the farmer who owned the hayshed near the dance hall, it was a much in demand location for after dance encounters.

I wonder if we had a reunion of patrons of the Castle Ballroom, who would laugh the loudest, would we laugh at all, or would we all be too embarrassed, remembering ourselves as we were? One way or another we all graduated from the Castle Ballroom. Some got married, some emigrated, and others simply retired through old age or infirmity. Sometimes when I pass the place nowadays, and I see the grass and weeds growing high along the walls, and the old weather-beaten door now firmly bolted against young dancers and part-time musicians, I think back on the joy the place gave us. In other towns and other cities there would be bigger bands and fancier halls, but for me the Castle was the launching pad and for that reason would always be special. In a way I suppose it too was a ballroom of romance, where, no doubt, love stories, and some heartaches did begin.

Cattle Fairs in Rural Ireland

T HE driver was desperately trying to edge his bus through the cattle, it wasn't easy, they were bumping into the sides and lowing up at the passengers who were taking in the scene with a mixture of amazement and fear. Forty Americans belting along the Dublin to Limerick road, they come around a corner and into a small town which has been taken over by cattle. Suddenly the Americans opened fire. As many cameras as would fit against the windows were blasting away at us. I'll bet that somewhere in California there's a picture of me standing in the middle of a few wild bullocks and we all staring at the Americans.

Cattle fairs are a thing of the past. The Mart, with its circus ring and the auctioneer, that sounds like a record that has lost the run of itself, has replaced the fair. It wasn't the most efficient way of selling cattle and it certainly made a mess of the town. But for one day every month it brought the place alive, in every sense of the word.

Six o'clock on a winter morning and pale lantern light illuminating a farmyard as cattle for the fair were rounded up. The long walk to town, here and there an open gate and a breakaway that had to be brought back to the road. Nostrils blowing, their warm breath visible on the frosty air. Here and there lights coming on and dogs barking as they sensed the passing herd. Dawn and the town and from every direction came cattle. Tired and a little quieter now, the journey having taken the fight out of them. The town was ready. Special wooden shutters protected shop windows and doors. The cattle buyers arrived, known as jobbers, they were men with dour faces and few words. Wearing high brown boots, trousers rolled up to the shins, they stalked the fair like sheriffs looking for badmen in a western town.

The first deals were done almost before the townspeople were awake. Men with fat cattle from the lush pastures of the lowlands sold easily, while men from the mountain waited for offers for their more bony specimens. As the morning wore on and the cowdung in the street got higher, jobbers' trousers were rolled further up. Deals were often hard to strike, maybe a fiver standing between a sale and another long walk driving a reluctant beast back to the field from which it had come. It was here that the middle-men came into their own. They were usually farmers who had made their own sale. Like bit actors, they would now have their few seconds of glory. Their stage the dirty street of a fairday town.

"What's between ye?" they would ask. "A lousy fiver," the jobber would say, as if it didn't matter a damn to him, and he having argued for half an hour over it. "Well split the difference", the middle-man would say, at the same time taking a hand of the jobber and the farmer and clasping them together in a symbol of agreement. The price agreed, the jobber would turn and head for the next deal, shouting back as he went, "turn them into the yard and I'll pay ya in the pub at three o'clock." Honour was saved on all sides.

In the centre of town, hugging the old courthouse walls, the dealers had set up their stalls. Clothes new, secondhand and of dubious origin were being measured for size against an assortment of bodies. The public street isn't the best place for trying on a trousers, but somehow they managed. At some of the fairs a coloured man with a van full of medicines turned up. He was commonly known as "the black doctor". Whatever the complaint, he had a bottle for it. Nobody ever died from his concoctions, at least not immediately. The psychology of his medicine must have worked for he would return again and do repeat business. It was pure coincidence that a certain undertaker sometimes treated the black doctor to lunch.

Late afternoon saw the streets cleared and the pubs filled. The jobbers paid over the money, sometimes demonstrating a slight lapse of memory on the agreed price, always on the downside of course. The stall-holders packed away the unsold goods for the next day in some other town, while a few farmers went home better dressed than when they left. The black doctor must have been happy too, knowing that the health of a few parishes in rural Ireland was about to improve. The pity was the Americans didn't get off the bus and savour the fair for an hour or two. They could have had some good stories to go with their pictures.

— O —

A Marshman's Last Post

A lot of the places that really appeal to me aren't to be found on any map, they're not considered significant enough to be recorded. It's a similar story with most of the people I've known, you won't find them in "Who's Who". People and places with labels on them are inclined to be somewhat unreal. It's the freerange type that tend to fire my imagination.

How is a man's worth measured? I'd venture to say that the conventional yardsticks would give you just about everything except a persons real worth. How do you measure a man's contribution when he is one who had rarely moved beyond the ditches that bound his own land? The Cahill brothers, Mick and Ned, were Laoismen. Their house was very small and everything in it was very basic. It had a galvanised roof which made a shower of rain sound like a world war. They lived in the townland of Barnadarrig, a place as remote as you would find. The laneway to the house is over a mile long. Here and there the trees meet overhead to form an arch, and if you drive a car up the lane the briars leave scratch marks along the sides. At the end of the lane the view opens out, and strange to relate it's at its most striking in winter. Had Constable passed that way he would surely have stopped and set up his canvas. It's a mixture of bog and marsh, brown and purple heather and green rushes, a few birches and the odd stately poplar.

I went back for another look at the place. It was late in the evening and so far from the main road that no man-made sounds could penetrate. A large red ball of setting sun was sinking into the heather. The distinctive sound of a curlew broke the silence. A lonesome sound, a sort of Marshman's last post.

There in the middle of the bog stood the remains of the Cahill home. Broken glass in the windows, the doors and roof gone, and the bare gables, their arrowhead shapes pointing skywards, like some sort of signpost to where Mick and Ned had gone.

A few hundred yards away across the bog, and half hidden behind a few trees, stood another deserted house, its roof and windows still intact, the Murphys, my mother's people. Rusting farm machinery littered the yard and a hare bolted from where it had made a home in among abandoned bales of straw.

At the other end of the lane the house that was Moores of Clunban.

37

Johnnie Moore drove his mother in a pony and trap to Mass in Shanahoe, three miles away, and during the Mass they left the pony tied in my grandfather's yard. Like the Cahills, the Moores have gone to their reward. It was in Moore's big kitchen, with the flagstone floor, that I first heard Mick Cahill sing. It was the night of a threshing — which is a story in itself. I remember that the beer was in a bucket and they were all dipping mugs into it, and Mick's song had a hundred verses, and no tune, and everyone clapped and asked for more. Mick was a shy man, he kept his gaze on his feet and chuckled to himself, and I have the feeling it was the high-point of his career as an entertainer. My mind comes forward to the empty, roofless house of today, and I remember it when it had life and smoke rose from the chimney like a silent aspiration. The Cahills gave me tea and in a mug that was so big I could hardly hold it, and the big hairy sheepdog that answered to the most common of dog names, Shep, would come over and lick the face off me.

The soil that made up the little farm was anything but rich, there was an endless tug-o-war with nature. Almost every winter the nearby river overflowed its banks, often leaving the little house totally surrounded by water. The animals gathered in around the house, standing apprehensively on the remaining patch of dry land. Like a twentieth century Noah's Ark ready for loading.

When the waters subsided and the elements were kind, the animals went back to the outer fields, while the brothers wrestled with the newly washed soil. I doubt they ever saw a television, they had no radio, and there was no electricity in the house. The greater world would not have been a place they would have been comfortable with. But that greater world would have been a place where one would have to search hard to find a pair of gentler souls. As I said earlier, how do you measure a mans real worth? Perhaps the universal scales will have only one question, what did we do with our allotment of the planet? What the Cahills did they did well, in the real sense of doing things. They gave back their fields none the worse for their tenancy, and I couldn't imagine that anyone was ever the worse for having known the brothers.

Soon the walls will be gone and grass will grow where a home once stood. Only those of us who knew the people who lived there will remember them, and the few trees they planted long ago will stand as their memorial.

— O —

Bringing home the hay. (Courtesy of Bord Fáilte).

The Village Blacksmith. (Courtesy of Bord Fáilte).

Everything Stays the Same

FIFTY years from now will the children of today look back nostalgically at the 1990's, remembering the old video films they used spend hours watching. Among the antiques in the livingroom of the year 2030, will there be a C.D. player and a video machine? I wonder if the middle aged Dubliners of the year 1060, weren't looking back to 1014 and talking about the great craic they had over in Clontarf, watching Brian Boru chasing Vikings along Dollymount Strand — or whatever it was called then. Maybe that Dubliner of long ago had an old sword hanging on his wall, a souvenir of the famous battle. Everything changes and nothing changes.

When I was a chisler the village was the centre of everything. Not many young people had cars, therefore we were limited by the range of a bicycle. A flashlamp was standard and a dynamo was upmarket. On a recent visit to the same village I saw the old men — and some not so old — standing outside the church after Mass. The very same heads that I saw there many years ago. I'd recognise some of them by the hats and the caps that they wore. Each with his own distinctive tilt, left or right, hanging off the back of the head or down over the eyes. The same hats and the same tilt, only the faces were lined and craggy now. This was the Sunday morning gathering, where you re-established contact with distant neighbours and then went your way for another week. The church, like a big piece of elastic, expanding during the week, each to his own task, and on the Sunday pulling all together again.

Inside that church things were much the same as they were in 1960. Well, with one exception. Back then the women were on the right and the men on the left, and never the two shall meet, not even if there was a shortage of seating on one side, while there were free spaces on the other. Today you go where you like, left or right. It took years to bridge that gap. It was at the back of the church that things hadn't changed. It was here that the men, shy of advancing as far as the first pew, took up residence. Spaces here were sacrosanct, down on one knee, cap on the other one, the mind wandering between things spiritual and things temporal. And the odd smart remark passed along, sending laughter ripples across the wall to wall boards. Through all the distractions and slight irreverence it was still a well meaning bunch. No doubt, He who rules over all must sometimes have been chuffed, if not a little amused, by his wayward backbenchers.

Up the village, at the garage, the young men of the 1990's sat on car bonnets watching the mechanic tune their engines. Thirty years ago their fathers sat on a pile of turf outside Ned Walsh's forge watching Ned hammer the red hot steel. Beating it into shape, sparks flying, the distinctive sound of the hammer on the anvil. Then a great hiss as the hot metal was cooled in the water, sending a jet of steam into the sooty, smoke-filled roof. Then picking up the horse's hoof and wedging it between his knees and with a pair of arms as strong as small trees he pared down the hoof and fitted the new shoe. Rump to rump they stood, him and the horse, each with a healthy respect for the other. From the forge to the garage, the stage and the play is the same, only the actors and the props have changed.

The village shop was once the mecca. Each evening after work, like the crows that came in to roost in the nearby beeches, they came to the shop. Lemonade, chocolates and ice-cream, bought on the round system. Discussion covered the spectrum: a post mortem on the previous Sunday's game, the prospects of a decent job somewhere else. Then some fellow spoiling it for you by telling the story-line of a film that was showing in town the following night. He having seen it while on a brief assignment with McAlpine's Fusiliers. They still come in in the evenings with the crows, chat still covers sport and the cinema and jobs, just add the disco and video. Only one slight change, the location has moved from the shop to the watering hole across the road, and the round of course, is all liquid.

If you go into the pub around either the longest or the shortest day of the year, when they are home for the haymaking or Christmas, you'll notice that not much has changed. The glasses tip and the greetings flow, and there's a hint of Camden town and Boston in the voices. Depending on who could afford the bigger fare. Around the surrounding countryside it would be hard to find a family without a relative in some far flung place. Just as it was for that earlier generation when they stood outside the shop across the road eating ice-cream. Outside the church after Mass in the 1990's, the young men who linger a while for a chat and to sniff the air coming up from the river, are pouring blood through the veins of an old tradition. Proof, if it was needed, that everything changes, yet stays the same.

— o —

Pitch and Toss

I T was a quiet Sunday afternoon when I walked up the single street that makes up the heart of my home village. Curtains were pulled back, and everywhere I could see the reflection of television sets. The street held no counter attraction, so the telly ruled O.K. Passing the old schoolhouse, long since closed, and the weeds now looking in through cobwebbed windows at the setting for many a young lads anguished youth. I was taken back to the days, before television, when Sunday afternoons were spent in the street. The gravelled ground by the gable wall of that school was the site for pitch and toss, a pastime that came into this century from God knows where, and died when the television took the thinking out of entertainment.

The game was simple. A small stone was placed on the ground, and from a distance of about six yards each player pitched two pennies to the stone. The player coming closest to the stone got to toss all the pennies first, retaining those which fell heads up. Side bets on the outcome of the tossing added the spice. The expression for being broke 'I haven't a tosser' possibly derives from that game. The tosser, from which the pennies were spun into the air, was a flat piece of wood about five inches long and an inch wide. And much as you will see a lad today with his personal cue for the billiard hall, everyone had his personal tosser.

It was very much a game for Sunday afternoons in winter, when the field was too wet for hurling. The village had three street lamps, and one of them conveniently lit the area by the school wall. Darkness therefore didn't close a game, it merely made a spot of cheating that much easier. Often when the light failed someone would go for a candle, and if a windless situation prevailed, the Las Vegas of rural Ireland would continue into the night.

It was an elite group that made up the pitch and toss school. Entry could not be achieved lightly. A lad could stand on the fringe for a whole season and never once be allowed in. Curlew Murphy was the 'club captain' and his word was law. He ruled in all disputes, and to challenge his authority was to risk joining the lads awaiting membership. Curlew wore a cap, and always in reverse order — that is peak to back. This gave him a somewhat comical look, which belied his godfather status. Pockets that bulged with pennies dragged his trousers towards his knees, like some second rate gunfighter from High Noon. We all wanted more democracy in the group, but no-one was prepared to challenge, and we weren't sufficiently skilled to stage a coup. And so we suffered the dictatorship of Curlew until one misty Sunday evening when the head of another school from a nearby townland joined in our game. He didn't require 'membership', it was automatic for a lad of his status.

Curlew was on top of his form, he was pitching with flawless accuracy, and winning bets like a man inspired. The visitor was more commonly called 'Hatchet', but never to his face of course. He was taking a severe ego denting, not to mention a financial hammering. The rest of us were mere extras, content to lose our hard earned pennies for the privilege of sharing the game with the two top dogs. Little did we know that it was to be the death-knell of our club. In the midst of the action Curlew jumped in and picked up a penny which had just been tossed by Hatchet. His face was a ghostly white, as were his knuckles from the tight grip he had on the penny. "Take a look at this lads," he said, opening his hand and doing a pirouette so we all could see. He turned the penny over, and sure enough, it had a hen on both sides. "A double headed penny," Curlew added. His acumen for politics was way behind his pitching ability. The electoral support he was expecting wasn't materialising, and before you could say 'Jack Rabbit', Hatchet had him airborne.

Intervention was not a consideration, there was a singular wish among the "extras" that they would destroy each other. As it turned out Curlew was almost demolished. Hatchet was a dangerous lad in peace-time, but now, as enraged as an injured bull — his cheating having been exposed — he knew that little further damage could be done to him. Stuffing all the money that lay on the ground into his pockets and taking a final kick at his adversary, he jumped on his bike. Then, like the cowboys in the local cinema, he rode out of town.

It was getting dark, the street lamp had come on and a light mist was falling. A coloured halo formed where the rain and the light met, and propped against the pole sat Curlew, rubbing blood from his nose. Outstretched hands offered to help him up, but he declined. He had suffered physical defeat and he wasn't going to compound it by accepting a hand up. The group formed a circle around him, standing in embarrassed silence with nervous hands driven deep into pockets. Democracy had come to the pitch and toss school. But like the demise of a king, the new condition left us wondering at the wisdom of our wishes. It was to be the last time I would ever see pitch and toss played in the village, or come to think of it, anywhere else for that matter.

— O —

The Story-tellers

I T had just gone midnight on a moonlit night and he was walking across fields taking a shortcut home from a neighbour's house, where he had been playing cards. In the middle of a field he was surrounded by hundreds of small people, fairies. All power to follow his own wishes left him and soon he found himself playing football with the fairies. The perspiration rolled off him. When the football ended they started to dance, and again he joined in. A fairy brought him a fiddle, for he must have known he could play, and on and on he played while the fairies danced. Then a cock crew and a tiny chink of light showed in the sky over Dunlea's field. The fairies had vanished, he was sitting alone in the middle of the field, a cold sweat on his brow.

That's the gist of a long and much more detailed story my grandfather told me as a boy. It was as real and as vivid to me as if I too had played football with the fairies. So vivid and real that today I have no problem dropping back into memory and recalling it in every detail. Today it's almost a cliche that television killed the art of story-telling, and I suppose that with the aid of some other modern methods of entertainment the claim is mostly true. It would be ridiculous to think that everything from the past was great, it certainly wasn't, but story-tellers were good, and today they exist no more.

They sat in a circle around the big open fireplace, pipes puffing like a railyard full of steam trains. They drank mugs of tea, poked the embers in the fire and now and then glanced at the big wall clock that ticked away the seconds. They told their stories with the seriousness of a courtroom drama. "I was walking home late one night from Kilbricken railway station," started my grandfather, and he went on to tell, how on a lonely stretch of road that passes over a river bridge, a priest had exorcised a ghost. Approaching the bridge he saw a small light shine every now and then. Again, like the footballer with the fairies, the perspiration rolled off him. There was no way of getting around this place, as there was no other bridge on the river for miles. So, being a man strong on religion he crossed himself and walked forward. The little light still flashed and disappeared. At the bridge his heart was thumping, then a voice said "good night," and the policeman sitting on the bridge took another pull on his cigarette before explaining to my grandfather the reason for his presence at that spot at that hour.

To this day when passing that bridge I think of the story. It is still a very remote stretch of road, and as a teenager I cycled it on many a dark night, always pedalling a little harder for that mile or so. I recall a night when the chain came off my bike right at the bridge. I spent a few anxious seconds getting it back on, while keeping one eye on the dark outline of the bridge, half expecting the ghost to place a cold hand on my shoulder. Such was the power of the fireside stories.

Tom Kennedy talked of the ghost that was often seen near the water-pump that stood on the road between my grandparents' house and his. "Very tall and always dressed in white," he would say, and adding, "and sometimes it walks onto the road in front of me." Then there was the night Tom was walking home past the water-pump and he almost got a heart attack when he looked and saw a tall white figure standing beside the pump. The figure moved across the road in front of him before discarding the sheet and identifying himself to Tom as a very earthly and living neighbour. Tom's bravado with ghosts had ended. All the while I sat there with my eyes out on sticks and afraid for my life to go to bed. There must be a lot of redundant ghosts and fairies out there somewhere. It's a long time since I heard of anyone seeing a ghost, and the fairies haven't had a football match for years. We are all the worse for the loss of the story-tellers.

— O —

Following the Wren

DRIVE through the country on St. Stephen's Day and you may see one or two young people wearing strange outfits and with blackened faces. They will go from house to house and their cry will be "Help the Wren." They are the last representatives of a dying tradition. The few who still follow this age-old practice nowadays, tend to be younger and far less colourful, in both dress and entertainment value, than in days gone by.

When we were about fourteen years old Christmas Day was good. Between presents and perhaps some new clothes, and lots of food, the young were fully occupied. But that afternoon there was a greater preoccupation. On the evening of Christmas Day we were putting the final touches to our outfits and our acts for the following morning. We seldom referred to St. Stephen's Day as such — it was commonly known as 'The Wren Day'.

I rarely remember the Wren Day as being wet. Occasionally there was snow, but more often, frost and ice. We were usually up before the sun and dressed in outfits from superman to cowboys and tramps. Drag was also a great favourite — it was also easy — it required only one of your mother's old dresses, and preferably your grandmother's hat with what looked like a basket of fruit on top. Balaclavas were also much worn then and they had none of the sinister connotations they have today.

It was a full day's work, from sunup to sundown. Mostly we travelled in pairs, pals tending to go together. It was a decided advantage if one could play a musical instrument, while the other attempted some lyrics. A good disguise was necessary, no-one should recognise you. I think this was the first big thrill of the event. Walking along the road on a frosty morning, meeting a neighbour who walked beside you with a puzzled look on his face, he trying to decide who was beneath the long red dress, and who owned the white teeth gleaming at him from a face that had been blackened by a burned cork. The neighbour would try to get you to speak, you wouldn't. You walked along together, eyeing each other, with only the sound of crunching frost beneath the feet.

Our signature tune was the same at every door, "The Wren the Wren the King of all birds, St. Stephen's Day he was caught in the furze, up with the kettle and down with the pan, give us a penny to bury the Wren." This was followed by a blast on a tin whistle and some lyrics that rarely matched the tune. It might be worth sixpence, or a bob, or even half a crown, if something in our act caught their imagination.

There was a hazardous side to the thing also. Some people who didn't particularly like young lads who followed the wren would put their fiercest dog out at the front of the house. The dog that was normally angry in the house, was twice as angry when put out on a cold day. And it was very difficult to run in a long dress, and even more so when a dog was biting lumps out of it.

As the day wore on we became tired from the many miles travelled and the sprints from wicked dogs, and the weight of accumulated coins. This was the point at which food was more important than money, and we were happy to do our turn for a slice of Christmas cake. I remember one such day, late in the afternoon and daylight fast disappearing and my buddy and I, two drag artists, sitting exhausted on the railway tracks of the Cork to Dublin line. We were sharing a turkey leg from the left-overs of somebody's Christmas dinner when we saw two 'cowboys' heading towards us in a determined fashion. It didn't take long to figure the possibilities, and we left the tracks as fast as any train ever traversed them. They chased us a bit, but the little headstart we had saved us, and we made it to the refuge of a friendly house. The cowboys — that's how they were dressed — were bigger than us and it wasn't uncommon to be relieved of your takings at the end of a day by a pair with physical advantage. The 'highwaymen' were usually from another area, and anyhow we couldn't identify them because of their disguises.

We always got home by dark and it was at that time that the real professionals hit the road. Groups of adults, often as many as ten, they travelled in vans, they dressed up as Red Indians, and had drums and short handled hatchets for tomahawks. They did a war dance in the street, they even had a few squaws with them. Having well entertained the village for half an hour, and made a generous collection from the pleased onlookers, they would adjourn to the pub, and like the words of the song 'the craic was mighty'. We weren't allowed into the pub, but we would peer in through the half open door. Little black faces that had their day, looking in at big black faces that were having their night. If we were lucky they would sneak us in when the barman wasn't looking, and a few bottles of lemonade would come our way. We would survive for half an hour, hidden under the table, until we were eventually discovered and sent packing. It's a pity that some traditions had to die, the countryside is the poorer for their passing.

— O —

Saint Fintan's Well

I T would be very hard for a stranger to find. The main road is such that two cars may only pass in safety when one of them stops, and the laneway that leads to the well is barely sufficient for one. The briars are overhanging and the potholes are deep. Then, in the middle of nowhere, a few tall evergreens. If you can get yourself as far as the trees you will be standing at Saint Fintan's Well in the townland of Cromogue about four miles from Abbeyleix.

Ireland is dotted with the wells and shrines of saints, each with its own legend and mysterious power. The first thing you notice about this well is how nicely it is kept. A few locals see to that, and the trimmed hedge and the neatly cut grass catch your eye as you walk the gravelled path that leads from a little green gate to the well. The statue of Saint Fintan has its back to you as you enter, he is looking across the moorland that sweeps away to the River Nore beyond. It is the quietest of places, the nearest living soul is a distance away. In this place the silence is broken only by the birds or the wind in the trees. A great place for a saint to meditate.

A low stone wall surrounds the well, and hanging on the arm of the small iron cross is a mug to permit the visitor to drink from the water. In the bottom of the well you see the sand bubbling, and the clear ice cool water gives you a pain behind your eyes. I can't say whether it's for real, or a thing of the mind, but I've never once left the place without a feeling of tranquillity. One other thing I always do is roll up my sleeve and reach down to the bottom of the well and collect a few pebbles. For legend has it that anyone who carries with him a stone from the well will never die by ship-wreck or by accident.

For generations locals have sworn by the curative powers of the well. A few of the older generation have never in their lives visited a doctor. Whenever some ailment afflicts them they go to the well and sip the water and invariably whatever the malady was it ceases to bother them.

When my mother was a child her father took her there. While he prayed she enjoyed herself looking at her reflection in the water. She leaned too far and toppled into the well. He fished her out, wrapped her in his coat and brought her home on horseback. The dousing in the good saint's well must have been good for her, for today she is in her seventies, and as they say locally, still flying.

In the last century, some miles away at Clonenagh, there was another well associated with Saint Fintan. It lay in the field of a local landowner who was annoyed with the numbers who were visiting, so he had the well filled in. Almost immediately it appeared about ten feet from the ground in a hollow·in the trunk of a sycamore tree on the roadside nearby. That tree is still there on the road between Portlaoise and Mountrath and the water is still there, high up between the branches. Passing motorists regularly stop to see the well, and again according to legend, they make a wish with the water and tie a little cloth or ribbon onto the branches. Unfortunately one other practice hasn't been helpful to the tree, they also bury coins in its wood by hammering them into it. You can see the evidence of literally thousands of coins that are in the tree and no doubt hastening its end. So respected is the tree that some years ago when major road alterations were being made in the area the tree was taken into consideration.

Saint Fintan and his well do for that part of the country what other saints achieve elsewhere. And it would be a fool who would scoff at any of them. For as Hamlet said to his friend, Horatio, "there are more things in heaven and earth, Horatio, than are dreamt of in your philosophy."

— O —

St. Fintan's Well, Cromogue. (Courtesy of James Yorke).

All-Ireland Day at Croke Park. (Courtesy of Independent Newspapers).

The Long Wait

IT would seem to run against the grain of nature, for a man to live the three score and ten, and never within that span to see the colours of his native county raised in Croke Park on a September Sunday.

My grandfather was cutting turf and I was helping him. As he worked he was singing a song about the Laois team that won a senior hurling All-Ireland in 1915. I was only a lad, but I was already well and truly absorbed with hurling, and all my heroes played the game. Therefore a song about Laois winning an All-Ireland set the blood flying to my young head. He pushed the spade into the turf and paused, "Do you see that man working way down the bog?" he asked me. I did indeed — he was tall and about the same age as my grandfather. "Well that's John Finlay, he was the captain of that team." If he had wanted me to work well, he had been unwise. Several times during the day I almost stuck the turf fork in his leg while snatching glances of John Finlay. And, old as he was, I knew the grandfather shared some of the pride. Were you at the match? I asked him. "To be sure I was" — that was always his way of answering in the affirmative. "Meself and Murt Horan rode there on a pair of horses, we took a bit of time at it."

John Finlay and the grandfather are long gone, and never since that day in 1915 did Laois win an All-Ireland. The grass grows lush down there and the cows milk well, the tourist passes through, but he never stays. For nearly half a century we haven't even got to play in an All-Ireland. Someone built a fine road through the county and the lads from Cork, Tipperary and Limerick were often seen flashing through with a big silver trophy in the back window. This must have triggered the thoughts of one bystander, who said "it was surely time for the famine to end."

In the towns, villages and bogs of Laois, men have waited for many a day. Being a county near the crossroads of the country we have often sniffed the air of the other man's feast as he celebrated victory. The youth who waited, and is now an old man, stands with another youth who waits yet again. He passes the time with words penned long ago by Peadar Kearney:

"When the whistle's gone and the game is on,
away with worry and care,
for the hopes and fears of a thousand years
once more are pulsing there.

There's a rhythmic clash as ash meets ash,
men fleeter than flying fawn
'Tis the symphony of the old ash tree —
The song of the brave caman."

Is it any wonder I have language difficulties with my friends from Tipperary and Cork. They don't so much talk about what they won, as how they won them — and of course the endless debate as to whether Mackey or Ring was the greatest. A debate as academic to a Laoisman as a wine list to a teetotaller. Still, "hope burns eternal" and year after year we followed the wearers of the blue and white, always to see them go down to the lads in black and amber or purple and gold. What is this thing that attaches a man to the county of his birth, that brings a savage roar from within his soul, and would make him abandon kith and kin to join the victory parade?

I once met a man who said it was all to do with the water! If so, it must be a strange pattern it weaves as it flows beneath Clonaslee, Borris-in-Ossory and Durrow, for when it goes a few more yards and fills the wells in Offaly, Tipperary and Kilkenny it deposits the properties that bring the gold. I think it's an old Indian proverb that says "don't judge a man until you have walked a mile in his moccasins." By the same logic the vanquished can't speak of the taste of the victor's cup.

But I heartell that a forge in the shadow of the Sliabh Blooms is casting a mightly cup. Why, you may ask, is such a delicate drinking vessel being cast in a forge. Well, only in such an establishment are there facilities for a cup that will have two inches of steel in its rim, so that when the day comes — as it surely will — and we are at last called to sup, every Laoisman alive and the ghosts of millions gone, will snap their teeth closed on that cup, for to drink will not be enough.

And little places with lovely names, like Rosenallis and Timahoe, will sacrifice a big tree, and the bonfires will tell their story, as they did for Patrick on the Hill of Slane. Only this time the High King won't come to put it out.

— o —

The Emigrants

TODAY people are going around talking about recession and depression and every kind of 'ession' you can think of. True, times aren't good and there's a lot of reason to be glum. But like the old saying "if you haven't tried it don't knock it." If you didn't live in the fifties, then you haven't a claim to a place in the first division. No doubt, people whose memories go back to the twenties, thirties and forties can make an even greater claim.

In the fifties in my home village and the surrounding countryside, if someone had offered a million pounds to the household without a relative in England or the United States, it would have gone unclaimed. They were the most uncertain times I can remember. Not just for the adults, but for the teenagers as well. Many a young lad had his first shave in England and that first miserable bit of stubble that should have gone down the River Nore instead ended up in the Thames.

Uncertainty stalked the countryside like a plague. Overnight you could lose almost anything, your father, your girl, your best friend. Everything worked in reverse to the way it should have. Summer and Christmas were the worst times. They always started good of course. Last year's flock of wild geese came home on holidays and the place was temporarily the better for their company and their affluence. But like so many things in life there's a price for everything. On their way back to Birmingham or London they had some other soul in tow. Most likely someone who had just recently fallen off the conveyor belt of childhood and some of us young lads had once again lost a friend.

We had a good hurling team, on and off. We would have had a better one had we been able to hold on to them. On a Wednesday the selected team for the following Sunday would be posted in a shop window in the village. It wasn't uncommon to find half the substitutes making the team by Sunday, the regulars in the meantime having gone across the big pond. If perchance we got anywhere near the final stages of a competition a particularly good player would be sent for. His fare home was paid from club funds and if I recall correctly it was never a great success.

The bit of travel seemed to have gone to the head and the game suffered. Or maybe it was that lungs polluted with the smog of London hadn't time to re-adjust to the rarified air in the foothills of the Sliabh Blooms.

The first man that I can remember emigrating still sticks vividly in my memory. It was a winter's night and freezing hard. The road through the village glinted in the frost from the light cast by the two street lamps. The one pub in the village had just closed and a group of men came marching up the centre of the road. It was the singing that caught my attention and I took a peek through the window. They would have been unsteady on a dry road, but that night the ice wasn't helping. The lad out in front was leading the chorus, "with my bundle on my shoulder sure there's no man could be bolder and I'm off to Philadelphia in the morning." The words he was singing told no lie. He was indeed off to Philadelphia the following morning and that was the last his home place ever saw of him. The place that gave him birth couldn't give him a living, and I sometimes wondered if perhaps some nights as he looked on the bright lights of the skyscrapers of Philadelphia, that perhaps for a moment, he could see in his memory, two village street lamps and a frosty road.

Today's emigrant travels like a boomerang, there's a return in every journey and parting carries none of the permanency it once did. There are those who never left the place. Just like the river that winds its way below the village, and the old mill that still stands beside the bridge, they lend a sense of time and place to things. They are anchors for the ones who still ride the waves. As you cross the bridge you hear the water going over the falls and the shadow of the old mill touches you like a comforting hand. In the village the pub and the shop are still there, though the names over the doors have changed. The old water pump still stands, though pumping no more and behind the hedge the tumble-down building that once was a school. Its walls hold the echoes of generations of young voices. All of this is what we left long ago and to which we return every now and then. Because no matter to where, or how far we roam, it will always be part of what we are.

— O —

A Visit to Inishmore

THE Naomh Eanna dipped and rose with the Atlantic swell as she carved her way straight out the centre of Galway Bay. The sun was shining, but a stiff breeze made a sweater feel comfortable. Cormorants, busy fishing, simply ignored our passing. On the right the hamlets along the Connemara coastline were coming to life, while to the left the coast of Clare led the eye to the majestic Cliffs of Moher. Straight ahead lay three humps in the water, like great whales basking in the deep Atlantic, my first glimpse of the Aran Islands.

The pier at Kilronan stood out like a defiant chin. The throbbing engines and the screaming gulls filled the air with sound, to a background of fast spoken instructions in Irish, as strong arms and strong ropes secured our floating transport. One mini bus and a dozen or so pony traps, stretched back along the pier.

Walking the half mile uphill to the guest house there was a sense of stepping back in time. I was already enjoying the Island feeling. This sterile area, protected from mainland malaise, by the Atlantic that washed between it and distant shores. The jarveys passed me, the horses maintaining their steady pace by the rhythmic reminder of a mild whip sting. Foreign faces with unsure smiles cast their eyes and their shadows across me and were gone. They sat bolt upright in the traps, contrasting with the drivers who sat as easy as sacks. At Teach Ui Bhiataigh it was nice to bounce my tired bones on the bed and later to feast my eyes on a golden sunset as I enjoyed fresh scones and a mug of tea.

The sun went down and the island went quiet. No neon lights here, only a soft half moon giving a silvery touch to the sea, and making it easier to avoid bumping into other mortals, as we made our way from one watering hole to another.

In the thatched pub, the man sitting on the beer keg had a fine voice and little change in years from four score. His lyrics told of the sea, currachs and a dark haired maiden. For twenty years he had worked on the buildings in England. The body went to London but the spirit stayed on Inishmore. Strong arms that built tower blocks for soul-less city gents were more at peace straining on the oars of a currach. He went from song to an Irish dance and the cold grey flagstone floor sparked like a half cracked match beneath his nailed boots. A small window, an old oak counter, an ancient picture of Killarney, long stools by the wall and beer crates and kegs for the patrons in the centre. A mustachioed barman, with a face like a saint, who could have doubled the price and hardly anyone would have complained. Only the bodies and the booze belonged to the twentieth century.

A few days on the island acted like an injection of cheek, and I found myself looking at the day trippers with a degree of annoyed tolerance. Most mornings I walked to the harbour. The quay was an open plan warehouse, a pile of timber, slates, cement, bags of turf and coal, oil drums and on top of them chickens in crates. A boat with a monster's head at the bow lay alongside, and bearded, muscular men passed cargo up to the quay. The engines throbbed, pumping life through its sea weary timbers, while giant jellyfish swam by, looking like underwater flying saucers. Out in the harbour six yachts lay at anchor, while a little away from them the bright orange of the lifeboat offered contrast, lying aloof and low in the water, like a sheepdog watching his flock.

Near Killeaney the airstrip was a tough breed of grass that kept the sand firm and allowed the little planes to hop in and out of the sky with the ease of sparrows. Nearby the wind funnelled into the bay and swept across the flat white strand, leaving the small roofless 7th century church up to its neck in sand.

Days when the elements were unkind mattered little, it was always dry in the pub. The mist brought its own charm, and when you couldn't see the mainland the island took on a new dimension. The fishermen came in and their fine vessels jostled in the harbour. The currachs of smaller operators huddled together on the rocks, their black bottoms up to the weather. Gulls, hungry for lack of fish, screamed their annoyance as they winged low over the water. Mountainous waves which had crossed the Atlantic met with their first resistance against the magnificent cliffs that guard the west side of the island. An angry sea and a defiant island in a duel of strength, that finally ends in truce, with a calmer sea lapping against the sun splashed cliffs, like teasing lovers after a fight.

'The best things in life are free'. Inishmore defines it well. Many's the hour I spent walking through soft sand and later looked back to find the sea had scrubbed the evidence of my existence. In contrast I walked down the backbone of the island, which is a barren limestone pavement. I found exotic wild flowers peeping through crevices, their roots drawing life from a modicum of soil wedged below, the ultimate in survival. There is nothing on Inishmore and there is everything, for you leave this last outpost of Western Europe with everything that's worth having and which you can always have with you.

— O —

The Skiing Farmer

THE rain was dashing against the window panes, threatening to smash in the glass. The wind howled around the gable of the house like a thousand banshees. Inside in the large kitchen the big Aga cooker glowed, to one side a kettle steamed gently, hinting at tea to be made. Myself, Denis and Margaret, relatives and old friends sitting in an assortment of chairs, some hard, some soft, in the comfortable atmosphere of the big farm kitchen, while outside the storm attempted to uproot the house. Little chance it had though, with foundations as deep as a well and walls as stout as a castle, this house withstood two hundred years of storms. The electric light flickered as the storm raged, but this kitchen was accustomed to flickering light. Over the centuries, candles, lanterns and oil lamps showed the way to generations of men coming in from the fields to their suppers at the big oak table.

I remember when the poles first appeared in the fields and then came the E.S.B. lines. The wicks on the oil lamps were turned down for the last time, and a one hundred watt bulb looked like the Blackpool illuminations, compared to what it replaced. Anyhow, back to that night. The door opened and a young man dressed in oilskins came in, followed by a sample of the nasty weather. John Joe, son of Denis and Margaret, was only a dream the night I first saw a bulb lighting in that kitchen. "You're working late, and in this weather," I remarked. "Cows don't give a damn how it is, they want to be milked and fed. Anyhow I'm trying to make up for time I missed over the past few weeks. I was away in Austria skiing." His father saw the disbelief on my face, "It's no joke, that's what he was at." I nearly fell off the chair. It seemed only yesterday they were digging holes, putting up poles and bringing power for the first time. This young man's father was working every hour of light that God sent him, and many of the hours of darkness as well. Now here I was meeting my first skiing farmer.

The oilskins dripping in the corner and John Joe toasting his toes against the Aga, he related the experience. It started with a couple of lessons at Kilternan, the purchase of thermal underwear and a pair of boots for walking around in the snow. The boots cost him fifty quid and there was no snow at all down at the bottom, so that was a bad start. The group was small, a few lads from Dublin, a couple of English lads and an English girl. The English lads were very daring, after only two days they ventured on the red runs.

And so the story went, the terminology of skiing was like computer language to me. "Red runs", how are you, it was a long distance and a far cry from the travels of my early days. No yodelling and cow bells for Peter and myself as we headed for Galway in an ailing banger. And between us we hadn't what John Joe paid for the boots. Out in Salthill we braved the Atlantic waves, tuned our ears to the foreign sound of west of Ireland accents, and we could just make out the dark humps of the Aran Islands away in the distance. It was another land beyond the sea. In the evenings, when it wasn't raining, we watched the big red ball of setting sun dipping into the sea, way out there towards America. At night the lights came on in the Seapoint ballroom and a smartly attired showband filled the hall with sound while the floor heaved to the swaying of a thousand bodies. This was no St. Moritz or Klosters, no sound of popping champagne corks, only the gas escaping from freshly opened lemonade bottles. It still puzzles me how that period came to be known as "the swinging sixties".

We survived that week, and I suppose the most exciting moment we had was when the suitcase broke loose from the roofrack of the old banger, and went hopping like a football along the main street of Kinnegad. Still, when we came back to Dublin we had been somewhere, and there was a story to be told. John Joe also survived his fortnight, not even a broken leg as a souvenir. On this stormy night he was already planning next year's encounter with the Austrian snow. It was a pity that back in the sixties that old banger wasn't capable of taking us to Austria. We might have lost our skis in Innsbruck instead of our shirts in Kinnegad. John Joe wondered if I might care to try it myself! "You know," I said, "I just might." Denis was laughing. He was thinking the storm had affected me. It hadn't really, it was just that in this kitchen I had seen the clock go full circle. The kettle was still steaming on the Aga. Margaret picked it up. "I'll make some tea," she said.

— O —

Saint Patrick gave us a Break

WHATEVER Saint Patrick did for Ireland, I doubt he ever banished snakes from our shores. This country is too cold for snakes. No self-respecting snake ever came within a thousand miles of Ireland. However, he did introduce us to Christianity, and with that came the season of Lent. Did you ever hear anyone under thirty asking "when does Lent start?" It's perfectly understandable that they don't. Today it carries none of the deprivation it did a few years ago.

When I was a kid, and that's not a hundred years ago, the feasting of Christmas was barely concluded when the threat of Lent arrived like a black cloud. Fasting was the first thing — 'one full meal and two collations', the Church said, and a collation wouldn't satisfy a healthy crow. Most of my ancestors were skinny and no wonder. I distinctly remember my grandparents and the black tea and butterless bread. If you tell that to the children of today they'll want to know if the old folks lived in the Ark. We didn't take it as serious as they did, but we gave up sweets and the men — well some of them — gave up the drink. The poorer of the publicans, without any religious motivation, had to subsist on black tea and butterless bread, until some of the lads cracked under the strain and went back on the drink.

Now one way or another, Saint Patrick was responsible for starting all this. When we youngsters complained, all we heard was that we were lucky we didn't live in the dark ages when people had to kneel outside churches wearing sack-cloth, and with ashes on their heads. Anyhow, Saint Patrick's Day tends to fall towards the middle of Lent, and it was accepted that hostilities such as fasting and no drinking would cease for one day. It was a sort of half-time in Lent. Not everyone got the old spirit wound up again to restart the hardship on March 18th.

In some rural parts no dancing was held during Lent. In an age when the dance-hall was about the only place opposites might meet, it was seven weeks of genuine penance. When Saint Patrick's night came around there wasn't room to breathe in the little tin shed we called the ballroom. If the publicans were starving, the man running the cinema was getting fat. His place was full every night and we hardly noticed the times the heating failed, punishment you see was now getting into the blood. It's fair to say that Saint Patrick's night was one of the big night's of the year. It would be equally fair to presume that it wasn't so much national fervour, as a sense of release from bondage, that had us all on a high.

Jimmy was a journeyman. Obviously he had a surname but I don't ever recall hearing it. Two or three times a year he'd appear in our area, do a little work, mostly for farmers, and move on. We kids liked him, he'd tell us stories of his exploits from Cork to Donegal. When he had a big one he'd start with "and once when I was in America." But when we tried to establish who he was and where he came from he had a line he gave us everytime. He'd say, "me name's Jimmy, I come from the Bog of Allen, I'm a wise man and I get drunk every Saint Patrick's Day." And he was true to his word. One Saint Patrick's Day, late in the evening, there was Jimmy, washing his face at the water-pump, one hand firmly holding the pump spout, to stop himself from toppling over. Flutered, as they'd say in that part of the country. And he shaking a finger at us and saying "I'll be a wise man again tomorrow." It's obvious now that not even Jimmy thought his life hard enough. He got caught up in the conventions of Lent and was merely having his half-time break on Saint Patrick's Day. I suppose you could say that like Jimmy, Saint Patrick, too, was a wise man. For if he offered us the bit of hardship to save our souls, then he gave us his feast day to break the journey.

— o —

Morrissey's

THAT which is old-fashioned is now fashionable, and to pass through Abbeyleix without a visit to Morrissey's is to miss an experience. The pub stands in the main street, it has been there for about one hundred and twenty years. Jet black exterior with the name, "Morrissey" embossed in gold. When you walk through the door you step back in time. For here is a pub where only the booze belongs to the 1990's, all else is as it was a century ago! A large framed photograph of the premises is captioned, "Morrissey's less a pub and grocery, than a state of mind".

I was sitting on the hard wooden seat, with the straight back, thinking, my grandfather sat on this seat, and perhaps even his father. The timber is stout but the front edge is worn away from backsides sliding off it, my ancestors, no doubt, contributed to the wear. Like all the wood here, it too is black. It was a winter evening. A large bearded man wearing wellingtons was standing at the bar. I noticed him eyeing me several times and then he strode over. He stood in front of me, swayed a little, and looked down at me "You're a bank manager?" he said. I promptly told him I wasn't. Just as well, for he had a major grievance with the man he mistook me for. Satisfied that I wasn't the bank manager he wanted, he turned to a lady and told her she was "the finest looking woman he had ever seen." It was a compliment, but who was going to protest. He turned back to me to tell me he had a bit of a farm. He added, "They say I'm an alcoholic, but I don't know." I asked how he felt in the mornings, "I don't give meself much of a chance to feel anything, I go back at it before the feeling gets time to start." With that he tipped his glass to me and went back to the counter. A poster behind the bar read: "When we drink we get drunk. When we get drunk we go to sleep. When we sleep we commit no sin. When we commit no sin we go to heaven. So let's all get drunk and go to heaven." According to that the big bearded man is headed for sainthood.

Every time the door opened a bite of the winter evening blew in, but the pot bellied stove in the middle of the floor glowed and took care of that. I had the feeling that the elderly men sitting close to it, had through the passing of time established claim to their places. Who knows, maybe one of them rode the 1930's bicycle, with the large basket in front, that now rested on a stand above their heads.

The grocery end of the counter was slack. Sweets in jars, a few newspapers, and an old balance scales, with a small pile of brass weights beside it. All along the walls the original shelves, and everywhere old advertisements. Fry's Cocoa, Will's Woodbines, Coleman's Starch and an add for "Gold Flake" that feminists wouldn't like, it shows two young ladies in an open sports car and is captioned, "The man's cigarette that women like."

Willie Joe Morrissey ran the place from the 1920's until he died in 1982, and there's a story told, of a bottler named Murray Anderson, who worked for him. One evening, Murray, with two bottles of beer buried deep in his pockets, was going home early complaining of being ill. Willie Joe offered him a pint to ease the illness, but Murray refused it. This gave Willie Joe to believe that Murray must indeed be very sick, so he took him to the fire and sat him down close to it. Soon the heat got to the bottles in Murray's pockets and the corks exploded. There's no record of Murray's career being dented by this incident. The old cash register that sits near the door may possibly have recorded a sale to Murray. It stands there still, with a farthing tab showing. There's a glass covered frame showing the names of staff since 1850. Beside it a photograph of a group of men sitting at the bar with their drinks, it is captioned "Past Pupils". I knew several 'past pupils' of Morrissey's who have long since joined Murray Anderson and Willie Joe, and if there's a sheebeen in the sky, I'll bet they're there. And that's a side of things that didn't go untended either, for out behind the pub Willie Joe ran an undertaking business. You can still make that final journey courtesy of Morrissey's.

It's a pub that links three centuries, a place where, should the ghosts of old customers return, they would still feel comfortable in familiar surroundings.

— O —

Tragedy for a Kerryman

EAMON Morrissey tells many a good yarn about 'The Brother'. In my case it is the brother-in-law who often comes up with a good one. A great follower of football and a Cavanman, Tom was a youngster tripping around the lakes of Cavan when the waters were unpolluted and the county had a great team.

But this has nothing to do with Cavan football, and everything to do with the game as played in Kerry and an ardent follower named Tadhg. It's a long time ago and it was a Sunday in September, and a very unusual event had taken place, Kerry had been defeated in an All-Ireland. Tadhg and Tom followed the play from the upper deck of the Cusack Stand. Sitting like a pair of black crows, they dissected every move. Football was serious business, and if a team did the right things they should win. Tadhg was programmed for anything except defeat for Kerry. You see it was a state of mind that he had never had any practice at. Success, like his right leg was always there, and if suddenly it was gone, so was his balance. Coming out of Croke Park it was raining and the green and yellow dye in Tadhg's paper hat ran down his face and he cursed the train that brought him from Tralee. He cursed with greater venom, as he put it, "the fifteen jackasses that couldn't kick their grannies off the Tarbert ferry". The brother-in-law was very consoling, but you can't resurrect the dead and Sam Maguire wasn't going to spend his holidays on the Ring of Kerry for the coming year.

In a well known drinking establishment, lying almost within the shadow of the Hogan Stand, Tadhg made an effort to drown his sorrows, but there wasn't enough time. You see it was in the days when pubs closed very early on Sunday evening. And all of a sudden Tom and Tadhg were looking at each other in the street and stone cold sober. But the hurt in Tadhg's heart was growing and he needed an anaesthetic and if the pub hadn't closed he could have had it. At this stage he turned to his friend Tom. After all, he was living in Dublin, he must surely have a solution to such problems.

There was a proliferation of clubs in the city around that time. Private membership and all that, places nevertheless, where a drink could be had on a Sunday night when other watering holes had run dry. But you had to know a member, and he had to take you in. If you knew a committee member it was better still. Tom knew such a man, Jem Clarke, at the John Redmond Club in Parnell Square, and looking at Tadhg he knew he was in need of intensive care.

There was a queue at the John Redmond Club. Tom advised Tadhg to put his green and yellow hat in his pocket. The allegiance of the doorman was unknown, therefore better to approach as a neutral, defeat didn't always bring sympathy. But, if there was a hint of Kerry in the doorman's accent the colours could be resurrected. The acceptance rate at the door was running very low, most of the applicants were as successful as beggars at a bank. Grown men were telling all sorts of lies and admitting to all kinds of connections for the right to pass the doorman. Tadhg nudged Tom and with a resigned look on his face, said, "looks like my agony is set to continue, a ghost couldn't get past that fellow." But the brother-in-law was confident. "I've been here before with Jem, it'll be alright." The door was closed all the time, except when it opened in short bursts and the seal of approval was applied to a lucky one. But mostly they were handing out rejection slips at the same pace as publishers to first time novelists.

Eventually the brother-in-law and Tadhg were at the top of the queue. The door opened, the brother-in-law spoke. "I'm a friend of Jem Clarke, he said that anytime I cared to come in just to mention his name." The doorman looked him in the eye, a relaxed look on his face. "Ah, no problem, he hasn't been in himself for some time, did you see him lately?" "About three weeks ago, met him coming out of a match," said Tom. "And how's he keeping?" asked the doorman. "Well I never saw him looking better," replied Tom. "That's strange," said the doorman, looking the brother-in-law in the eye again. "Jem died two months ago, but if he's looking down on you right now I'm sure he's laughing, and for that you may come in." And so it was that a Kerryman's pain was relieved.

— O —

66

The Olympic Champion

IT was 1956, the year that British and French troops invaded Egypt after Nasser nationalised the Suez Canal. In Budapest Russian tanks crushed the Hungarian uprising. Rocky Marciano retired as undefeated heavyweight champion of the world, and Marilyn Monroe married playwright Arthur Miller. Now none of those events had much impact in our little village. Jobs were scarce and emigration was rife, we had enough problems at local level to keep our minds concentrated.

That summer we played hurling on the village green and when winter came went indoors and were entertained by Din Joe on the wireless. There was no-one without a relative working in England and every week another name or two was added to the list. Another winter of discontent was settling in.

On the other side of the world in Australia it was high summer, and at the end of November the Olympic Games opened in Melbourne, the first time they were ever held in the Southern Hemisphere, not that that mattered much in our village. But what did matter was that a young man from Dublin had made it to the final of the 1500 metres. Ron Delany was standing at the door of athletic history. There was no television then, but a crackling radio signal brought the event across the world to us. The Irishman had won gold in the blue riband event, the 1500 metres. It was a day or two before we saw the picture, Delany on his knees on the track his head bowed to the ground, and the great Australian athlete, John Landy, bent over him in a gesture of concern.

That win was like a tonic for the nation. Even in our village jobs and emigration became secondary topics for a while and every young lad who could muster a trot was being called Ronnie Delany. But there was another treat in store, and for a few minutes Melbourne was coming to us. Returning to Ireland after the Olympics, Ronnie Delany flew into Shannon and travelled by road to Dublin. In every town and village on the way crowds turned out to greet him, and we weren't going to be left out. There we were, halfway between Limerick and Dublin and all down by the village green waiting. The school band, the teachers, every villager who could drag a leg, and men who had a sense of history in their blood left their fields for a few hours on this once in a lifetime day.

The entourage appeared, the band struck up, hands waved, men who had been leaning against bicycles dropped them on the grass, freeing their hands to applaud. The cars stopped, Ronnie jumped out and bounded across the road to where we were waiting. Behind him came the press photographers. Here on the little green where we played our hurling Ronnie took the gold medal from his pocket and showed it to us. A few words here and there, a few handshakes and he was gone.

Shortly afterwards a nice photograph of that event was hanging on the wall of the local school. That was all a long time ago and some time back I called to the school to see if the picture was still there. I met the current teachers, they were both young, their parents may well have been among the youngsters on the green that day in '56. There were pictures on the walls but not the one I was after. "There's some behind the press, Sir," a young boy said. The teacher asked that they be brought out, and a half dozen young lads dived in, delighted with the distraction from the routine of lessons.

Out they came with pictures of the old castle, the old school, pictures of everything, and then the one. A large framed picture, Ronnie Delany, head bowed, wearing a light coloured duffle coat, the medal in his hand. On one side the teacher, on the other, four wide eyed boys, not looking at the medal but at Ronnie Delany's face. At the back a few villagers, and on the grass the bicycles.

I mentioned that it was an historic photograph, the only time ever that Ireland won Olympic gold in a flat race. And here was that man on the green outside our school showing us the medal. As I left the school they were preparing to put the picture back on the wall.

— O —

Delany prays having won the Gold.

The Threshing. (Courtesy of Bord Fáilte).

Memories of the Steam Thresher

R IGHT at the edge of my memory is the picture of a small group of men with a horse pulling a cart full of gravel. They were going along a narrow country road shovelling the gravel into potholes and tapping it firm with the back of the shovel. No, they weren't working for the County Council — although indirectly you could say they were. They were merely ensuring that the steam engine and threshing mill would make its way safely from Dunleas to Murphys. It was quite common for the big cumbersome engine to sink into a pothole, and perhaps for good measure to smash something as well. It was a time when some country roads had only a gravelled surface, held together only by the ditches that bounded them, and at the mercy of the elements, invariably full of potholes, and as such a danger to man, beast and machine.

The combine harvester is efficient and labour saving, and long may it live. But the old style threshing was a joy to behold, especially with a steam engine. It was more than a job of work, it was a celebration. Summer had come and gone, the corn had turned from green to gold, Autumn leaves were drifting down and the corn was now in big ricks in the haggard. The field mice were building homes underneath, unaware that their tenancy would be a short one.

The entourage arrived like a circus. The steam engine drove into the haggard at a speed that would make a snail seem like a four minute miler. It towed the threshing mill, and the mill towed the straw elevator and behind the lot walked a handful of men with hay forks on their shoulders. Like a bunch of undisciplined soldiers, they straggled behind, their faces grave. From farm to farm the platoon would go, a mixture of volunteer and conscript. It was the done thing to assist at your neighbour's threshing.

In between the ricks the machines moved, perfect alignment between the mill and the steam engine was necessary, otherwise the belt might fly off the drive wheels and possible decapitate someone. To maintain the tension, and stop the machine from moving, big blocks of wood were hammered into the ground in front of the wheels.

In the big country kitchen the crane over the open fire was at full stretch with suspended pots full of bacon, cabbage and spuds. The men in the haggard were lean and strong with matching appetites. The old steam engine had a hunger and thirst of its own. Beside it stood a heap of turf for the fire in its belly and a couple of barrelfuls of water to maintain its head of steam.

The slow turn of the wheel, the first movement of the drive belt, the first revolution of the mill drum, a sort of curtain up. Then faster and faster until the hum of the mill drowned all conversation. Feeding the mill was one of the key jobs. The sheaves were pitched from the rick onto the mill platform. The man feeding had a very sharp knife. In one swift and rhythmic movement he slit the twine binding the sheaf and spread it across the drum. As the mill chewed up the corn it shuddered and roared like a dinosaur. Clearing the chaff was a dirty job, and always assigned to some young lad.

The first lull came a couple of hours into the work. A big cream coloured earthenware jar full with porter was carried out. Mugs were passed around and the dust was washed down. The young lad on the chaff got a bottle of lemonade, and the smarter of the field mice started to emigrate. The whole scene was one of a small industry come to life on this one day per year. Sheaves of wheat flying from the rick to the mill platform. The swift touch of a sharp blade, the twine severed, then the hungry growl of the mill as it gobbled the sheaf. Straw cascading down and rising again on the elevator to form a new rick. Sacks hanging on hooks and the golden seed pouring in, and the young chap lost in a cloud of dust trying to keep the chaff cleared. The engine driver adjusting valves, stoking the fire, topping up the water, and with the ever present long nosed oilcan guaranteeing the smooth running of all moving parts. Now and then a spark from the chimney, quickly chased down before it started a fire.

As the sun went down and the last sheaf left the ground and the last mouse made a bid for freedom, the lights glowed yellow in the house beyond. An aproned woman, silhouetted in the door, calling that the tea was ready. Across the big table talk was of how good the yield was, and how the sun went down in a red sky, tomorrow would be a fine day. Afterwards someone brought an accordian. A few neighbouring women arrived and the dancing and singing started. There was no evidence of tired limbs as the house now vibrated almost as much as the thresher had done earlier. Tomorrow would be another day and another farm.

— o —

Train Travel

FASHIONS come and go and what was worn yesterday will be back again tomorrow. My first ramblings through Ireland were on trains and nowadays I find myself taking to the rails again quite often. With today's hassle on the roads the train is an efficient and relaxing way of getting around. But it's much more than that, it isn't just that you can sit back, read your book and mark the page three hours later as you step out 150 miles away. There's a culture on the trains and there's the back window world train travellers pass through which is never seen from the road.

We are all characters on the stage of life, but on the smaller stage of the train carriage you sit back and watch the unscripted show unfold. On a train from Killarney two nuns sat side by side, eyes closed, lips moving silently, rosary beads running through their fingers. A chap with a ring in both ears was giving a back-packing Dutch lady a very distorted political and economic view of Ireland. Now and then their conversation stopped and they watched the nuns. The nuns prayed on oblivious. An elderly lady who was knitting kept throwing furious glances across at a young man who had his feet up on the seat in front of him. Finally her anger overtook her restraint and she addressed him. "Would you do that at home, put your feet up on a seat?" The lad was taken by surprise, he whipped his feet down and buried his head in his walkman. The lady with three children could have done with a carriage to herself. The baby wasn't yet walking, but on its hands and knees down the aisle of the carriage it went as fast as one of Ger McKenna's greyhounds. Big brother, all of about seven, was instructed by mother to "bring Jimmy back." And twenty times he brought Jimmy back and Jimmy was getting better at escaping every time.

Railway stations are mostly old buildings that retain their character, the features that in the early days of the century made them exciting places, the equivalent of airports today. Stopped for a few minutes in these stations and looking at the cut stone buildings and the latticed windows, the old iron foot-bridges across the tracks and the dilapidated waiting rooms that don't seem to be used anymore. The setting made it easy to visualise the train travellers of yesteryear. The steam train belching its way into the station and women in long dresses and men in caps and hard hats waiting. Many of the little stations are closed now, grass growing on the platforms, windows boarded up, and the train now shoots through in a few seconds.

Like something that didn't want to remember that this was once a place from which people travelled.

Travelling by road the eye is ever meeting the presentation side of houses, the fronts. Neat gardens, painted hall doors and nicely curtained windows looking out over tidy hedges. From the train it's the other side of the coin. From the back there's no chance of thinking that the place is deserted. Back doors are open, curtains are drawn back. You feel almost like an intruder, as if you could open the train window and say, "excuse me, but I was drawn in here and I'll be gone in a few seconds." I could have said that to the man in his pyjamas cooking at a stove in a kitchen, or to the elderly lady sitting at a fire with a cat on her lap. It's the living side of houses, caught in their nakedness. Unpainted walls, downpipes like protruding veins, the odd old cooker or washing machine, its life now done, waiting for its final resting place. And the clothes lines, the very personal marks of human existence.

Back on the train there's a lot more elderly people than some years ago. This is to do with free travel for the over sixty-fives, it's a marvellous idea and a credit to the country that provides it. The lady from Limerick was coming to Dublin to see her daughter, she would go back in the morning. The man from Kerry was also coming to Dublin to see his daughter. He was telling his life story to a young American girl, and she was writing the details in her diary. "And write down that you met me, Peadar, and I'm seventy five and I'm going to Dublin to see my daughter, she's a nurse, a grand foxy haired girl, and I don't have to pay a penny for travelling." The American did his bidding. At Heuston Station all the little stories poured onto the platform and scattered themselves all over Dublin.

— O —

74

Power Failures and their Consequences

YOU have to be a certain vintage to remember a time when you went into a shop, called out your list of requirements to the assistant who then roamed the shelves and placed the items before you on the counter. In those pre-calculator days the prices were then pencilled in and the verbal totting up was done. Shop assistants wore brown coats and always had a pencil on the ear.

Now what has that got to do with a power failure? Not a lot I suppose. But one night recently when a fuse went and I was left in the dark, the first thing that came to mind was the E.S.B. strike of last year. I was in a supermarket and the place was functioning nicely with small camping lamps here and there. In fact the lamps changed the atmosphere of the place and it temporarily took on an old world appearance. However, at the check-out it was a different scene, confusion reigned. Without power the cash registers weren't working and the check-out assistants were completely at sea without the aid of their calculating machines.

About fifteen years ago I was in Moscow, and having purchased some food items in a hotel I was amazed to see the cashier tot up my bill on an abacus. It seemed like a hundred years ago since we learned to count using one at school, and here was a lady operating one with the speed of a calculator. I don't care how some may decry it but it's still useful to be able to calculate in your head using old style tables. But back to the power failure. The T.V. was gone, candles weren't good enough for reading, even if they did cast long shadows and make it seem as if Christmas had come out of season. The transistor came into its own. Not alone did it tell us when we could expect to be able to boil water for our next cup of tea, but we were once again introduced to the many wonderful programmes that go out on radio during those evening hours when nowadays the television rules and the voice in the radio is silenced. It was a reminder for me, and I am sure for many others, of just how good radio can be. Like the old saying, "It's an ill wind that blows no good."

My bedside clock was just a black face where the green digits used to be. Out came the old alarm clock, it had been in retirement for about fifteen years, appearing only in emergencies. The ticking seemed as loud as Big Ben, but it was a remembered sound and instead of being annoying it almost amounted to company. My neighbour has one of those new fangled remote phones. He goes around the place from bathroom to back garden cordlessly in contact with the world. That is until the juice ceases to flow, and then in keeping with the Christmas atmosphere of the candles it becomes "silent night". But my old black phone sitting on the hall table, remote from everywhere except the little box it's attached to on the wall, is still chirping away. And my neighbour is very thankful and has some doubts about electronic progress.

The street lights were gone and you only saw the car in front of you by the lights of your own. It was a rural scene temporarily come to town. I don't seem to be able to get away from the Christmas scene that it evoked, for here and there and everywhere through uncurtained windows one could see the inviting light of big Christmas candles, now pulled into off-season service to meet the emergency. On one evening I was too hungry to wait for the return of power to get something to eat. So an old black pan came out and filled with rashers and sausages I trust it upon a fire of peat briquettes. Not since long ago, when I ate food similarly cooked over an open fire in my grandparents' house, did I eat anything that tasted so good. Power strikes are definitely a problem, but like all negative things if you look at them hard enough they very often have a positive side.

— o —

The Big Oak

S TANDING, sentry like, on top of the hill, the big oak was visible
from all directions. It was reckoned to be about three hundred and
fifty years old. Shakespeare was possibly still alive when a pair of
hands dug a hole and placed in it a small sapling, which grew to be a big
oak. Three and a half centuries later it was still standing. Three hundred
and fifty times this planet had gone around the sun and the old oak tree
was on every trip.

In present times, when talking to plants is accepted by many as being
beneficial to their growth, to express an affinity with a tree would not seem
strange. But back in the late 1950's it would indeed have been cause for
concern were a body to declare such oneness with a tree. I had a thing
going with the big oak from around the age of six. I was even prepared to
forgive the several times it let me fall to the ground from its lower
branches. As I grew older I climbed higher, establishing a geography of the
tree for myself, locating a dozen different places throughout its branches
where I could nest and watch the rural world go by.

The hill dropped away to the fertile valley and climbed again to the
Sliabh Bloom mountains beyond. Just below me the river Nore meandered
its way from the same mountains on its journey to the sea. When trouble
brewed at home, or elsewhere, and the weight of the world rested on my
young head, I would take myself away to the tree. Finding solace as I lay
hidden deep in its protective arms, whispering my troubles to the rustling
leaves. When eventually I'd come down and make my way back to face the
music, I was invariably less fearful of my fate, as if I had been fortified by
the God of the forest.

I was about twelve years old when I felt a great necessity to stamp my
identity on the big oak. With a wood chisel and hammer I carved my name
in foot high letters, cutting through the bark and deep into the sap wet
timber. The tree must have cringed in horror at the mutilation I was
inflicting on it. I watched it over the years as new growth gradually eroded
my name, as if the tree was gently rejecting my declaration of ownership. It
would offer me what I wanted, but it would also be a place of refuge for
any man or beast which might shelter beneath its outstretched branches,
from the cold of winter or the heat of summer. It was a special thrill to
dash in beneath its cover during a heavy shower and listen to the raindrops
as they crashed against the leaves that formed a giant umbrella. It gave me a

sense of security as I fixed my eyes on the border-line where my circle of dry earth met the unprotected area beyond.

On summer evenings I would often take a book, climb into a spot I liked to think of as my reading seat, and drift into a world of my own. No armchair felt more comfortable, nor would the story be as vivid if read elsewhere. And any story I read, whether fact or fiction, if it was set at any time after the year 1600, I would look at my tree and think, 'well, you lived during that period' and I'd imagine what size it was at that particular year.

Even the crows, possibly through some natural instinct, seemed to sense the history of the big oak, as they battled each other for a building site in this oldest of nesting neighbourhoods. On a spring day the tree was as busy as Picadilly Circus, as little black flying machines shuttled in and out with building materials. Later, when the eggs were laid, I'd climb to the topmost branches, risking life and limb, for a peep into the nests to check the progress of the new black fliers. The parents circled nearby, screaming in protest at my impertinence.

The night of the storm was also in the spring. I remember thinking that it was going to blow the roof off the house. The storm died with the night and the dawn revealed a minor trail of destruction across the country. I met my friend, Andy, on his way to work. He didn't pause, he just shouted at me "did you see the oak? It's down." The pain of loss was instantaneous. I was now eighteen, memories flooded back, it was as if a strong and silent friend had died. It wasn't just a landmark, it was an anchor, a shelter, a summer house, a reading room, an open-air confessional, and the home of many crows. I walked to the hill, there it lay, roots exposed to the heavens for the first time in three hundred and fifty years. Motionless, no rustle in the leaves anymore, the crows' nests crushed beneath the splintered branches.

It made several lovely fires that year, and a local timber merchant took away the trunk — perhaps there's a piece of fine furniture somewhere still from it. To this day, whenever I visit the place, I look at the spot where the oak once stood and I remember that tree. I remind myself that art lives beyond the artist, and if I haven't the talent to paint a picture or write a poem, perhaps I can plant a tree. Then someone who may walk this earth three hundred years from now will send good vibes to my spirit, as I often did to the one who planted my oak.

— O —

The Pull of the Sea

THERE is only one county in Ireland that doesn't touch a county that touches the sea. It is Laois. It was the land of my youth, hemmed in between the bogs and the mountain, between the soft turf with its carpet of purple heather and the mountain. The mountain that went chameleon like from green to blue as the changing light rolled across it like a conjurer's hand. The river came rolling down the mountain, crashing over stones in its foamy and hurried descent. In the valley it got deeper and wider. When it passed beside our village it was silent and genteel, having spent its energy on the mountain trip.

When we were kids the pull of the river was as steel to a magnet. In summer, swimming and catching minnows in jam-jars, in winter watching the salmon struggling against the waterfall as they tried to make their way upstream. It was the only water we knew, and how were we to know, as we romped through the reeds on the banks of the Nore, that one day the pull of the seas would all but obliterate the magic of our river paradise. I was about ten years old when I first saw the sea. At that age everything appears big, but the great expanse of water that was spread out before me was something else. The soft sand under my feet felt as comfortable as a feather pillow, and the lovely 'swoosh' sound the water made as it lapped around my ankles. In it came and then out it went again, as if it couldn't decide where it wanted to be. Then as if by some kind of magic, the pages of a story-book had come alive, there on the horizon was a ship, getting bigger and bigger as if growing out of the water. At school Brother Declan had just taught us a song with the lines: "Far away places with strange sounding names, far away over the sea." Right there and then in my child's eye those far away places had come home to me.

Search as I may I've found no logical explanation for the pull of the sea. It is as if some primordial thing lives in it and lives in us, and is ever drawing the two together. Man has challenged the sea and been victorious. But like a lion with its cub, it is merely being playful, allowing us to indulge in our childish challenges. Every now and then it bares its teeth and demonstrates its awesome power, reminding us that we are no more than the grains of sand on its wave lashed shores.

Off the Cape of Good Hope lie the angriest waters in the world, where the Atlantic and Indian Oceans meet. Old sea dogs have cringed and cowed before waves of mountainous proportions, and the seas have opened in a

79

giant black hole, swallowing ships as would a whale a minnow. On a more local level, near Slea Head on the Dingle Peninsula, I saw the remains of the "Kanga" tossed from the sea like a seed on the wind, its back broken on the Kerry rocks. A reminder to all that you ride the waves, not by right, but by concession. Then, by contrast, to walk on Dollymount Strand, as I often do, and to see the children with their buckets and spades, dogs chasing bits of timber into the surf while seagulls ride the air currents that sweep into the Bay. And others, like myself, stroll along the beach allowing the mystery that is the sea to envelop us in its tranquility, and make restful, minds burdened by the cares of life.

As eternal as the stars that guide the sailor and with moods to match the best and worst in man, the sea yields up enough to keep us all alive. I go down to Howth and watch the fishing craft come in. An honour guard of airborne seagulls escorting them to the quayside, their rewards for escort duty, a little portion of their silvery, slippery catch. Night falls on the harbour, and the boats anchored side by side bob gently and rub shoulders and the lighthouse winks across the dark deep waters as inviting as a Christmas candle in a window.

I remember a place in Kerry where the meadow rolls down to the sea, where the seagulls and butterflies meet. Where one could lie in the long grass on a warm day and be lulled to sleep by the gentle sound of breaking waves. From the same spot I've watched a storm break-up, the clouds moving fast across the Kerry hills and the sun splintering the skies with colour. Far from the concrete jungles and the maddening crowds this quiet place down by the sea stands like an anchor to time. The murmurs of the ocean echoing the morning of the world. Whether it is watching the sun peer from behind the hill of Howth, as its first rays dash across Dublin Bay, or far from home seeing the big red ball being cooled as it dipped into the Indian Ocean, the sea is still magic and a mystery.

— O —

Gaelic Scotland

AS a young lad, to me, Scotland was a mysterious and far away place. A land of castles and mist, dark lakes and blue green mountains, and of course bagpipes. Sure enough the dream and the reality matched. Something in the Scottish spirit is akin to that of the Irish, and you can feel it, almost as sure as you can smell the heather on the wind when you reach the Western Isles.

The sun was low in the sky, the waters of Lough Lomond were ablaze with light, dozens of boats were gliding gently to their moorings after a day on the lough. This was the small town of Balloch, gateway to the highlands. Accommodation in a farmhouse was not at odds with the tranquil surroundings. Beams in the bedroom ceiling, a bed with brass ends and porridge for breakfast, and for good measure the waters of Lough Lomond almost lapping against the back wall of the house. I asked one of the guests, a Londoner, if there was much Gaelic spoken in Scotland? "None at all," he told me. How wrong he turned out to be.

After breakfast, down by the water's edge, Duncan Macauley was sitting on a log skimming stones along the placid water. There wasn't another soul in sight in any direction. Streaks of early morning fog ran down the lough, and way out in the centre of the dark waters a small island with a halo of fog sitting above it. Conversation was easy, this was no crowded city street where people meet and pass in silence like cans on the conveyor belt of an urban existence. Macauley had been to Ireland many times, had fished on Lough Corrib, played his tin whistle in a pub in Dublin, and attended the Wexford Opera Festival. Enough credentials for honorary citizenship. He was waiting for a boat to take him to the island. A friend of his had some holiday chalets there. There was a scrap of history attached to the island, Mary Queen of Scots once visited the place. Would I care to go across? I would indeed. My plans for the morning were instantly changed.

Returning from the island and going northwards towards the Highlands the winding road snaked its way following the contours of the Lough. Stopping at a viewing area to take in the scene, and with the car door open, I sat on a big stone listening to a match from Croke Park. Across from me on another stone sat a piper, kilted and wearing a beret, his pipes silent under his arm. He asked me where the football was from? "It's hurling," I told him, instantly regretting that I had made the distinction. "Indeed,"

81

said the piper, "the game comes from our shinty." He had me, I couldn't say who borrowed from whom. A bus-load of tourists pulled in and the piper stood on his stone seat and started to play. All the way to Glencoe the lonesome notes lingered. Again the scene was repeated, on another hill another piper played, and the music, like the shadows, drifted through the glen, while the hills went from green to purple in the changing light.

In a pub in the glen two elderly men spoke in Gaelic. I understood a few words and this was enough to make me feel some sort of affinity.

Over the sea to Skye took only ten minutes by ferry from Kyle of Loughalshe. On Skye the roadsigns were in Gaelic and English. By the roadside men cut turf in shallow bogs, and elsewhere others made haycocks in small fields. Shades of the Ireland of yesteryear. Down in Portree, the Island's capital, gaelic was being spoken everywhere. In the town square, over the bank, beside Bank of Scotland, was Banc na hAlban, over the Post Office, Oifig a Phoist, and on the street sign, Cnoc na Gaoithe. That Londoner back at Lough Lomond hadn't got it right.

As the sun went down the little harbour filled with fishing craft. From a hall on a height over the town came the sound of ceilidh music. In the pub the pipes played and songs in Gaelic and English filled the air. Here on an island to the west of Scotland visitors from many lands were rounding off a pleasant day. For me it was more special still, it was the only time outside of Ireland that I ever felt totally at home. Somewhere in the distant past we were the same people, and in the time between we haven't moved very far apart.

— 0 —

Observations at the Airport

WE met on the escalators, I was going up and he was going down. "Hi, where are you going?" he shouted across at me. "Nowhere," I replied. He shrugged his shoulders in a gesture of confusion and we drifted apart to different floors of Dublin Airport. My friend's question was fair enough, it's reasonable to assume that someone you meet at the airport is going or coming from somewhere distant. I wasn't, I was merely seeing off a relative and carrying a suitcase for her, that was as heavy as herself.

For me, it's not a chore to go to the airport. Living at the edge of Europe, at arms length from the continent and a world away from the next landfall across the Atlantic, we tend to be a little insular. Brown, black and yellow faces are not as common in our streets as they are in London or New York. If it weren't for the Spanish students we would never hear a sustained burst of a foreign tongue. That's where the airport comes in, it's like a window on the world. A visit there is the next best thing to going on a holiday. Although it's only a piece of land sitting on the edge of town, yet it is one of the crossroads of the world.

The terminal building sees more drama than a Broadway Theatre. After all, the stuff on Broadway is put-on, an act, but at the airport it's all for real. Just sit in the arrivals area and watch the joy on the faces, as friends and relatives meet after lengthy separations. See the anticipation that has been building up for weeks, maybe months, all released in a few seconds of pure delight, as they spot their loved ones coming from the customs hall. Cases flung down, arms outstretched, feet swinging. The only thing bringing them back to earth for a moment is the tingle of glass, the duty-free booze, "Oh God did I break it!"

Upstairs in the departures hall it's the other side of the coin. Red eyes, tears and heavy hearts. The arms are outstretched here also but the feet stay on the ground. Words are fewer and whatever talk there is, is unrelated to the moment and gives no hint of the hurt within. Small personal gifts, held to the last minute, now being pressed urgently and silently into hands that are reluctant to take. Beyond the ticket gate noses pressed against the glass and a final wave of goodbye. The sky above the airport should be full of rainbows from all the tears and smiles.

Watching the holiday makers come and go is a different story. No agony and ecstasy here, just a bag of craic. They are all gathered in a huddle, like a rugby team at half-time, have you got your ticket, your boarding pass, the right label on your case, otherwise you are in Terrimolinos and the case is in Toronto. Now drop downstairs and watch the crowd coming back. No sign of the courier, the apartments were such a disaster that she is gone into permanent exile in Mongolia. But look at the tans and look at the blisters! Chemist shops from Leixlip to Limerick will do a roaring business for the next few weeks. Then there's the last minute exchange of addresses and phone numbers and promises to get together soon. But that's what they did last year with a different gang, and there'll be a new lot next year. Holiday romances and friendships are as stable as melting snow.

The monitors keep flashing departures and arrivals to and from all parts of the world. The public address system asks if Mr. So and So, a passenger from Singapore, would please contact the information desk. For a minute you can wonder who he is and what he is and what he was doing in Malaysia. All a game of wondering and in the end most of it will remain a mystery.

Five in the morning and all is quiet, the silence broken only by the hum of the floor polishing machine. A young couple sleep, propped against their back-parts. The car hire desks are lit, but empty, the bank is closed, the grill is down on the flower shop. The security man sits in subdued light, his electronic testing equipment on the table in front of him. Out there on the roads and in the skies today's travellers are preparing for the international exchange.

Watching planes rising from the runways, a trail of water spray behind them before they disappeared into the rain-laden clouds. Beyond those clouds the sky was blue and the sun was shining and I wondered at the many places they would touch down. A man going out threw a red rose in the bin, perhaps from someone going away, that didn't mean as much to him, or maybe someone that never turned up. It was a cold day and walking from the airport beside me was a man in Nigerian dress. Outside the door he looked at the sky and gave a shiver. The airport is a world in miniature.

— o —

The Burren in Winter

FAIR weather friends are many and I suppose the same is true of tourists. But a visit to a popular resort at a time when it is most unpopular has its own rewards. Like the back of the moon, it's the side we never see. It was late evening in February and a watery sun was dipping into the Atlantic. There was no traffic congestion in the streets of Ballyvaughan. The two telephone booths in the square were empty and only the menus in the windows of the closed restaurants and the remnants of posters from the previous summer, gave any hint of the metamorphosis that would take place in a few months time.

I had come to see the Burren at a time when even the birds had gone to Africa. And yet, like a fire smouldering beneath the ashes, there was life in the place. Outside the window of Monk's pub the gulls were swooping low over the water, while inside flames from a turf fire leaped up the chimney. In the background the low sound from the radio told of traffic jams in Dublin. At that minute in that street in Ballyvaughan mine was the only car. I cupped the warm drink sitting before me on the stout table of clear pine. A collie strayed from behind the bar, its tail wagging, took a look around and seeing that all was well with the world, retreated. Not for the first time I wondered at the wisdom of my living in the city.

Next morning I drove thirty miles in the rain to meet a man who puts words together, in as colourful a fashion as a garden of flowers, only to discover that he had gone to where I had come from. I learned this from a man I met leading a very big bull at the end of a piece of rope. They're brave men in the county Clare.

I had never been to Lisdoonvarna. Its famous spas and match-making festival I'd read of and seen on television, pictures of a town bursting at the seams with fun and hope. Not so on this Saturday afternoon. Wind driven rain washed the deserted streets as the last of the weekend shoppers moved with bowed heads against the elements. To get a bite was difficult, all the eating places of summer were still deep in their winter hibernation. But at the Roadside Tavern music leaked through the door.

Inside an inviting fire and a group of musicians playing with gusto for six young Germans, who must surely have fallen from the skies. All round the walls postcards from all over the world, yellowing from smoke and time. On a mantelpiece evidence of the mild winter, a bunch of daffodils duplicated in a mirror. Overhead an old clock ticked away, a quarter of an hour ahead of actual time. A German asked the barman about the clocks inaccuracy? "It's to do with closing time, not always easy to get them out on time." The visitor was puzzled but he left it at that. Back in the wet street a dog sheltered in a doorway, perhaps dreaming of the leaner days of summer.

At Doolin Pier the Atlantic spray was shooting into the air like the geysers of Iceland. Further along the coast, despite the rain, I walked across that unique flatbed of rock that is the Burren. Here and there on the tables of rock the scrawled messages of visitors. People who left their mark, not so much as graffiti, but more like candles lit at a shrine. On one big rock one word, "peace". I'll have to go back when the flowers peep from between the stones and the Atlantic has lost its anger.

A pub near Fanore was another oasis in this winter wilderness. The big log fire made coming in from the weather a real pleasure. In front of it a slice of timber straight from a tree topped a barrel, two black pints sat on this novel table, their elderly owners made way for the newcomer. "A rough day," said Tim. I told him it was much worse in Doolin. "Any nice girls there?" he enquired. His companion, John, cut in. "Never mind that ould fella, anyhow if he got a girl he wouldn't know what to do with her." Looking over his pint at Tim he told him "It's praying for a happy death you should be." A young lady came to the fire and John told her that Tim was a fortune teller. She was curious and presented her hand to Tim. Tim took it and bent it in all directions examining the patterns. "He's going to tell you that you'll be seeing a bonesetter," said John. There was fortune and good health and travel in her hand and of course a pint for Tim. The barman passed an armful of logs out over the counter, "lob them on the fire there John."

Tim was curious as to what I did for a living. John whispered in my ear, "tell him you're a tax inspector and that you're interested in his income from fortune telling." Tim had other worries, he was convinced that a neighbour had murderous designs on his cat. All in all the kind of scene that if lifted to a stage would pull any audience. Even with rain sweeping across the Clare hills the Burren still has its winter magic.

— O —

The Burren. (Courtesy of Bord Fáilte).

A Corncrake.

The Plight of the Corncrake

THE corncrake is on the verge of extinction, at least in Ireland. With the exception of areas in the West and in Donegal the bird is rarely to be found in the rest of the country. An elusive and shy bird, seldom seen but so easily identified by its harsh rasping call. So far from melodious and capable of keeping you awake at a mile distance, that one would wonder why it is much loved. Only a few years ago they inhabited every meadow in the country. That was in more leisurely days before farming technology moved to its present state. Progress is defined as "an advance to something better." In the modern world it's a word that all too often represents the opposite.

I can only account for myself, but I'll always associate the corncrake with country places and warm summer nights. That distinctive sound; craic craic, craic craic, coming from the meadows as they called and answered each other. We were kids then and we learned that they came to us from South Africa. That was a far off and warm place and we wondered about how they could fly so far. I remember sitting on a field gate with a friend on a moonlit night trying to identify where the sounds were coming from and guessing at how many were there. Years later that same sound was evocative of warm summer nights and the smell of new mown hay, as if the bird brought with it the warm air and the blue skies of South Africa and in a way I suppose it did.

When something is lost forever we all die a little with it and no less so when that something is a species of bird. I don't feel that we were born for the concrete jungles we inhabit. Tranquility carves a deeper path to the soul when we are closer to the long grass and the rushes that is home to the corncrake. But if our concrete jungle adds nothing to our betterment, at least it remains a safe place, something we cannot say for the home of the corncrake.

And that brings me back to that word again, progress. The fields are sprayed with chemicals and nature is the first to suffer. Silage machines suck up the grass and often the birds that hide in it. Intensive farming has meant that fields are grazed low, leaving no cover for the birds.

The number of corncrakes in Ireland today can be counted in hundreds and that represents twenty percent of the entire European population. But there is something that can be done to help protect them. Meadows are traditionally cut from the outside in ever decreasing circles and the corncrakes are driven before the machines into that last remaining piece in the centre where they are destroyed. If the cutting started at the centre and worked outwards, the birds would be forced towards the ditches and safety. Maybe here and there small patches might be left so that breeding may continue. A little goodwill would go a long way and it would be a small price to pay to bring back a bird that may be standing on the brink of extinction.

About four years ago on a Saturday morning I was walking through woods in the hills beyond Dublin. Here in the silence the city beyond was a far off place. A light mist fell in this quiet spot, the silence broken only by the hurrying of a small stream on its way to join the river below. Bending over the stream with cupped hands pouring the cool clear water over my head and face — a thing I like to do in such places. At that moment I heard a cuckoo; that beautiful, haunting, lonesome sound that seemed to come from here, there, and God knows where. It was back again in memory to an almost forgotten time. It was many years since I had heard a cuckoo and I haven't heard one since. Like a photograph, a moment frozen in time. The destruction of the rain forests are big events, but like the longest journey, their preservation must start with a single step. So whether it is a flower or a forest or a cuckoo or a corncrake, now is the time to think about them. Tomorrow may be too late.

— O —

Saint Anthony

HEAVEN, is no doubt, full of saints, and most of them must be pretty busy interceding on behalf of their earthly clients. A few of the very obscure ones don't find it necessary to have clinics at all and they enjoy a very relaxed existence, spending their days playing their ever in tune harps. But for the busy ones, this heaven is almost a hell. And who can be busier than Saint Anthony, the poor saint never gets a rest. Morning noon and night they come, seven days a week. The requests pour in to him, the anguished cries of the despairing and the frivolous. Around his statue in our church a heat haze rises from the mass of candles burning at the Saint's feet. It must be a most uncomfortable alcove with all that heat. On Tuesdays it gets even worse, for today everyone wants to light a candle. And when all the candle holders are full they still light them and place them on any space they can find. The priest advised that the practice was dangerous, but the warning had little effect. Nobody was prepared to take the chance that their aspiration would be heard without the lighting of a candle. The risk of burning down the church was a secondary consideration.

All around the church, in other alcoves, other saints are freezing for the want of a few candles. The pews in front of them lie mostly empty, while in front of Saint Anthony as soon as a vacant space appears another pair of knees drops in to fill it. By the way, Anthony, was the name he adopted in religious life, as a young lad he was known as Fernando. He was born near Lisbon almost 800 years ago and died in Italy in 1231, at 36 years of age. He is buried at Padua.

He must never get to his heavenly bed, just maybe the odd nap on a cloud. But as soon as he is dozing off, another tug at his toe. A job urgently needed for Johnny. Pat wants honours in the exam and he never studied. Mary wants her husband to come home and Joan wants to get rid of hers. The candles are piling up and the heat is unbearable and poor Anthony is wondering why he ever accepted sainthood and the responsibilities that go with it. As he sits pondering his luck, Saint Patrick walks by with a golfbag under his arm and a sprig of shamrock in his cap. Anthony shouts after him; "Eh Paddy, you're the patron saint of this lot, how come they're not bothering you?" And Saint Patrick glances back over his shoulder and points to the shamrock, "I left them this little puzzle, and anyhow I was a bishop, they'd need an appointment to see me."

My mother is a real big fan of Saint Anthony, and when I say big I mean big, like everyday all the days of her life. She will swear that all of the family were often snatched from the jaws of danger through her influence with the holy man.

On a recent visit home my keys were lost. Every obvious place was searched and no luck. "Say a prayer to Saint Anthony," she said. Well, a few words to Anthony about the keys and, hey presto! there they were under my nose. Not bad, I thought. As I left the house my mother said, "and don't forget to light a candle for the finding of your keys." I was going to explain to her that the poor man couldn't stand any more heat, but thought better of it. An old lady that I know in Dublin, she has a path worn to Saint Anthony's statue in the church and the strap on his sandal worn off from touching it. She wanted her hippy style globetrotting son to come home and settle down. We met in a shop, she had a big smile on her face, "he's back and he has a job," she told me. She knowingly added, "you know who took care of that?" And who better to appreciate the predicament of a wandering Irishman than Saint Anthony? He left his native Portugal at an early age and travelled through Morocco, France and Italy.

There are miracles attributed to him during his lifetime, but as soon as he died stories of his miraculous intercessions just poured in. So much so that within a year of his death he was canonised a saint. Although he never wandered to Ireland, his influence did in a big way. I always knew him as the saint who found things. Obviously he takes care of other things as well. Judging by the candle power in front of his statues in churches all over the country he is coming up with the goods. He has an eye to the little, comical trials of life as well as the heavy ills. There is a rhythm even in worship; saints come and go in popularity but the cult of Saint Anthony is universal and static throughout the ages. There isn't much hope of him ever getting a peaceful heavenly day, unless of course he changes his name back to Fernando. In which case he can go golfing with Saint Patrick.

— O —

Memory

"THERE seems something more speakingly imcomprehensible in the powers, the failures, the inequalities of memory, than in any other of our intelligences." So said Jane Austen. It's almost like a claim to fame to say you're forgetful, everyone seems to be in on the act. The majority have good recall, I, unfortunately, am in the other category. My sister reminds me of something I said to her thirty years ago and I can't recall what I said to her last week. If you don't suffer from it you won't appreciate the pressure it can put you under. Names, now there's a real problem, because it's an everyday thing, and terribly embarrassing when someone you meet almost daily greets you by name and his or her name won't come to your tongue. There must be many out there who have considered me distant, or even unfriendly, when I didn't respond by using their names. What they wouldn't have known was that I was dying a thousand deaths trying to recall their names. When I had gone a hundred yards past them the name came to me and I felt like kicking myself with the frustration.

Of course it doesn't stop at names, it's the word memory in general. Dates, places, events, they'll come up alright, but not when you want them. It puzzles me how the photographic memory can be so good. Another one that works very well for me is sound. A voice on the phone, even from long ago, and bingo, I have the name. You can feel very isolated until you find a few fellow sufferers. This doesn't help the memory but it takes away the feeling that someone might decide to have you put down.

John, a friend of mine, goes to work on his bicycle. He got up one morning, made his breakfast, put the teapot lid on the tea caddy, that was a bad start, he was a mile or so down the road when he realised it was Saturday. But I know of a man who had a worse experience than that. He had changed house and a month later drove back to his old house, parked in the driveway, and only when trying to get a key into the door did it dawn on him that home was now elsewhere.

Another one I know of, is of a man driving his very drunk friend home. The driver doesn't know that his friend has changed house, so he takes him to where he used to live. The friend doesn't remember he has changed, he tries the key in the door and it won't turn. His memory is good enough to recall that when he has turned up drunk before his wife had the night latch on, so he starts throwing stones at the top window and shouting "ah jaysus

93

Brigid open the door". When the window did open two very embarrassed men left the scene.

There's a sackful of books written on how to improve your memory and I've read a good few of them. But it's a sort of "catch 22", you'd need a good memory to remember them. However, there are a few things that can help. For example, go through the alphabet and when you come to the letter that starts the name or word, half of the time it will come to you. The other method, and it can sound a bit ridiculous, is association, but it does work. Create a mental picture of the person in association with something that rhymes with their name. The more ridiculous the association the more likely you are to remember the name. A man I meet every now and then is Pat Holland. Long ago I made my picture association for him, I see Pat with his finger in a hole in a big Dutch dyke, holding back the sea. After I run that image through my head the name, Holland, is easy. On his shoulder I see a cat, and when I meet Pat he is never aware of the vast amount of strange computing that has gone on in my head just to say hello to him.

A man I knew well, who is now deceased, early in his life he married and the marriage lasted only a few days. Many years later he married again and very soon found himself charged with bigamy. His defence was that he forgot about the first marriage. The judge didn't believe him.

There is, however, a positive side to having a poor memory. Old movies, I've seen some of them three times and each time the plot reveals itself almost as if for the first time. Now if only the bank manager would get a bout of that which afflicts me and forget about the few bob I owe him, since me forgetting about it doesn't seem to help at all.

— O —

Sounds

MUSIC must in some way or other be connected with a dimension beyond human comprehension. Perhaps reaching out and bringing man into some sort of harmony with his origin somewhere deep within the universe. Music seems to be a key that connects us to a higher consciousness, sometimes creating a euphoric state that transcends earthly experience. A gift open to the wise and foolish alike. Otherwise how can you account for someone like me? I love music, in particular the violin, and yet I wouldn't know a note from a sack of coal. There I am singing away to myself for personal entertainment and this friend of mine laughing at me. "Can't you hear yourself?" she asks, "you're changing key on every word." Making music seems to be harder than listening to it, and sure who knows, maybe the pleasure of sound is a matter of interpretation.

One of my grandparents lived near a railway line and from my stays there I have two abiding memories related to sound. Now you would never see as many telephone wires anywhere else as you would along a railway line. There they were suspended in silence from pole to pole, carrying messages up and down the line, words unheard by our ears as we lived our days just beneath them. But come a stormy night and the wires came alive. A thousand instruments rising and falling with the wind, sweet notes and sad notes, piercing and frightening. Then the soft sound as the wind dropped, and you waited for the maestro's baton to rise again and for the orchestra of wires to again sing in unison. The other sound is that of trains. Just a murmur as it approached and then the explosion of sound as it passed you, and finally that clickity click, clickity click drifting away to total silence again. Sitting there watching this little world on wheels, with a sea of faces at the windows, as it spent its few seconds in your life.

Out there in that same countryside, away from the railway tracks and the wind in the wires, there were the hundred other sounds the wind made as it brushed against nature's obstacles. Such as a field of ripe golden corn as it did a Mexican wave and the soft rustle as the wind blew across it, like the ocean waves breaking gently on the shore. You asked yourself where it came from, and the answer was there in the words of the poem. "It comes from fields so far away, the wind that shakes the barley." A wild wind that came from God knows where and filled you with its music before moving on to the blue beyond.

Birdsong, in particular in spring, is a world apart. There they are singing for themselves and for anyone who cares to listen. The top of the wood is alive with a halo of sound. Even down to the little suburban back garden they come. A smaller number in the chorus here, and standing on top of the tree the blackbird is king. Black feathers heaving, yellow beak open, pitching notes in all directions. A concert to match anything that man can put on stage. Then the hour when all is silent down in the woods, so silent that you think you can hear it, but it's only the sound in your own head. There's a great peace in moments like that and it lasts until the wind stirs the topmost branches again, reminding you that time has passed.

For years I went to sleep and woke up to the sound of cascading water. That hypnotic sound that only varied as the river went up and down with rainfall. The waterfall was no Niagara, but it was constant and it must be buried in my sub-conscious, and sometimes when I listen to a small stream babbling along I remember that river and the constancy of the waterfall.

Sounds, like smells, are evocative of things past. A kettle whistling on a kitchen fire. The echo of a church bell coming across a valley, a factory horn at the end of a working day. The ring of a hammer on an anvil, clearly audible half a mile away, and what about the greatest sound of all, the ocean? I know many people who say they could not live away from the sea. I have lived, and I still could live away from the sea, but I am always happier when I am close to the sound of breaking waves washing the shore or the roar of a storm tossed sea crashing against the cliffs. Vision is half of life, sound is the other half.

— o —

Language Problems

READING Paul Durkan's poem 'The Drimoleague Blues', the first few lines took my mind off in another direction. It starts, "Oh I know this town is not always mean. And I know that you do not always mean what you mean. And the meaning of meaning can both mean and not mean." It set me thinking of the inadequacy of language. A definition for inadequate is 'short of what is required', that's the closest I can come to the meaning I have in mind. It's the 'in mind' bit that gives the problem.

Now before I begin to sound complicated, let me elaborate in a fashion experienced by us all. Is there a person alive who hasn't had some friction with another and all because, to use a common phrase, 'they took me up wrong'. What was said was misread, the wrong meaning taken. It happens all the time. When all is peace again it's quite common to hear the parties to the misunderstanding say, "you know that wasn't what I meant at all"; to which the other replies, "oh yes, but I should never have taken it up that way." The argument ends with both of them shouting Mea Culpa and all the while the fault perhaps lying with the language.

To prove this point there is no need to search for extremes, or to dig out statistics. It's sitting there in almost every word of every language and we are the victims of it almost every day. Language, whether the spoken or written word, is our principal vehicle of communication. It carries us through the routine functions of living and now and then in crisis situations we are forced to dive in with a degree of urgency. Words have to be carefully selected, speedily assembled, then transmitted to another mortal in the hope that peace will be restored.

How long is a piece of string? Well don't bother to think about it, it's as long as you like. What is hot, what is cold? It's whatever you conceive it to be. We are always searching for the right word, but what makes it the right word? It will be the right word when the interpretation placed on it by the receiver matches precisely to the intent that triggered the word in the transmitter's head. Or simpler, when what I mean is what you understand.

There is a theory that early man, before he developed sounds for communication, could read the other person's mind, right down to the finest emotions. This of course must have been very useful, it eliminated complicated explanations. By the same token it isn't hard to see how dangerous it might be. Then as man developed from grunts to sophisticated sounds he became lazy and neglected practising hi wonderful gift of mind reading. Today we are left with the remnants o that power, those moments when something is said, which you wer thinking about, or perhaps you were thinking of a certain song an someone starts to sing it, or a person comes to mind and the 'phone ring and it's them. How often do you hear it said in relation to a good speech 'my God, I wish I was half as articulate as that'. For articulate the dictionary says 'capable of clear expression', for clear read 'plain, distinct obvious', for expression read 'revelation by language'. As you can se there's no end to it and no meaning to it either.

'It's an ill wind that doesn't blow some good'. The failure of language to have precise and singular meaning may sometimes be a blessing. It allow the makers of foolish statements to extricate themselves, to utter that face saving line that might prevent anything from international conflict to a domestic row. After all look at what politicians can talk themselves int and out of. And what about the fellow who comes home somewhat of balance at three in the morning and says 'he was held up at the office' There's a lot of interpretation in 'held up'. Then look at the language o law; learned men spend years pondering on the wording of legislation They emerge chuckling at their airtight handiwork and a week later some young whizzkid barrister, with more flair for language than law, drives the proverbial coach and four through it.

Poems and songs lend themselves to great flexibility of interpretation; words that cause no emotion in one person may move another to tears. It's all to do with the inner eye that converts the words to pictures and that's simply a matter of interpretation. There's no guarantee with language, no matter how carefully you select your words, it's still up to someone else to decide how they'll interpret them.

Next time you're with someone and they are not exactly pouring words at you, watch out for that other language; the shoulder shrug, the raised eyebrows, the little cough that isn't a cough, the adam's apple being swallowed. Now that's real language. It's a close relation of the mind reader from long ago, and it very definitely means what it says.

— o —

The Night the Lights Went Out

IT was a hot, sticky evening, Wednesday, July 13th, 1977. New York, the Big Apple, was sweating its way into the night. Air conditioners hummed and the lights along Broadway winked at each other. It was 9.30 in the evening and then the lights went out.

An hour earlier a thunderstorm had swept across the green suburban hills of Northern Westchester close to the Indian Point Nuclear Power Plant overlooking the Hudson River. Lightning knocked out the lines and the power station automatically shut down. Minutes later two more supply lines in Westchester were hit and engineers at the control centre in Manhattan scrambled to balance the load. Further lightning strikes knocked out other supply lines, the loss of power had a cascading effect and by 9.30 p.m., New York and 9 million people were in the dark. It took a while before the reality of the situation hit home. Some Broadway shows continued under the beams of flashlights held by stagehands, while the nude cast of "Oh Calcutta" unable to find their dressing rooms, borrowed clothes from members of the audience and made their way home. The street was now the stage and a twenty-five hour drama was at act one.

The Mayor of New York, Abraham Beame, was making a campaign speech in the Bronx and like many citizens, he assumed a fuse had blown. He joked "see what happens when you don't pay your bills." A few hours later he declared a state of emergency in the City of New York. So much for blown fuses.

To a visitor, New York is intimidating even when you can see where you are. At that precise moment I was absorbing the atmosphere in Time Square. It seemed to me like all the world had gathered here, and since there were so many and not enough space to spread out, they had forced themselves upwards into the skyscrapers that towered above me. A friendly New York Cop was guiding me through the maze, "see those two broads over there," I looked and had started to admire the nice lines when he added "they're guys." I had seen Danny La Rue, but never on the streets and it was at that moment that New York went black for me. Within the first few minutes I heard several voices curse "Con Edison", I was wondering if he was some kind of saboteur until my friend removed my ignorance by advising that they were referring to Consolidated Edison, the Power Company.

The good humour and joking that greeted the first minutes of darkness was short lived. Opportunity seems to bring out the best and worst in man and long before midnight the streets were teeming with tens of thousands of looters and plunderers. Men, women and even children were ripping steel shutters from store fronts with crowbars and everything they could carry was being taken away and what they couldn't remove they destroyed. The cry "It's Christmas time" echoed through the ghettos and by the following morning over two thousand stores had been looted.

In the Ace Pontiac showrooms in the Bronx, looters smashed steel doors and stole fifty new cars. Men walked casually along the streets carrying large items of furniture while others tried on clothing for size and style. The arsonists were as busy as the looters, over a thousand fires and twice as many false alarms, mostly to divert the attention of the police and sometimes just for the hell of it. Water gushed from fire hydrants and swept the residue of the looting into the centre of the streets. The police did their best, but it was like trying to stop the tide, it simply broke all around you. Some looters were so cool they went over to fire engines and quenched their thirst from the running water and then back to fill the truck they had backed up to the store window. Many thieves were in turn robbed by others and they were heard to complain that "it shouldn't be allowed."

The hot, humid night continued and with it the orgy of destruction. The police couldn't win and they didn't expect to. They were pleased to break even and that meant a kind of compromise, like the kid carrying a box who was stopped by two policemen. He dropped the box to the tinkle of glass "What's in the box Johnny" asked one of the policemen? "Booze man, liquor," replied the kid. "And where'd you get it Johnny?" "I bought it man, paid money for it." Peering into the box the policemen saw that the markings on the broken bottles were from a looted store. "Take the box and go home and maybe you can do us a favour some day."

Some of the action was high in the air; thirty-five people spent the night on the 86th floor observation deck of the Empire State Building, while 500 people finished their meal by candlelight in the restaurant on the 107th floor of the World Trade Centre. In Shea Stadium the play stopped, and 20,000 fans sang "White Christmas", to take their minds off the heat. Some taxi drivers were asking five times the rate for a fare to the suburbs, while a few enterprising youngsters guided old ladies to their apartments for a dollar.

Daylight on Thursday found parts of the city looking like a battlefield. Store owners were nailing sheets of plywood to windows that fronted empty shops, while groups of youths, all wearing new sneakers, watched in puzzlement. "Christmas is over," someone said.

Out in the suburbs, in the residential areas, not much had happened, a lot of people missed the air conditioning and couldn't sleep. Freezers went soft and the kitchen was closed down for a day. A lot of people didn't go to work that Thursday. By ten o'clock that night Con Edison was back in business. For the looters from the ghettos it was the end of the midsummer Christmas. For many from suburbia it was the night love stories began and for a visitor from Ireland — despite the hassle — it was a bonus to be in New York on the night the lights went out.

— o —

Words

We say not what we feel
And we feel not what we say.
Words are little arrows
We fire at each other everyday.

Most of the chatter is just
Bait cast on the blind.
Probes to see what's happening
In the other fellow's mind.

Sometimes giving away a yard
While planning to win a mile.
Not for a moment realising
This is also the other fellow's style.

At the end of each conversation
You're little wiser than before.
Truth, hangs not on the periphery,
But is spinning at the core.

The greatest language spoken
Is as silent as the dead.
It's when hearts start talking
And not a word is said.

The Hitch-hiker

I T'S always easier to part with anything when it's at its worst, and leaving Ireland is hardly an exception. Packing your bags for warmer shores on a miserable wet day gives an added dimension of pleasure. The Spring morning I have in mind was far from miserable. The sun shone bright on a sleepy Dublin Sunday, the streets were almost empty, and the lovely cherry blossoms through the south city stood like honour guards as I made my way towards the ferry at Dunlaoghaire, en route to the Middle East.

Holidays were over and it would be two years before I'd set foot in the Island again. All the romantic notions of far off exotic places were pushed aside by the reality of the moment. "The savage loves his native shore," and right there and then I had no problem identifying with him. But the contract and job was out there, so go I must.

The spires and skyline of Dunlaoghaire dipped further into the horizon and my eyes scarcely blinked lest they miss that last glance, and every second a little more of me died, and I wondered at the wisdom, if any, of it all. Finally the land and sea merged, there was nothing to look back at anymore. It was chilly on deck, so I went inside and had some warm coffee. I cast my eyes across the faces and suitcases of my fellow travellers and guessed at the stories that lay behind tight lipped smiles on this peaceful Sunday morning.

Sitting there thinking to myself, they'd be getting up in Dublin now. In kitchens tired limbs would be stretched while bacon sizzled on pans, while in the distance a church bell tolled. But then it was back to reality, and I was driving off the ferry and heading down through Wales towards Dover on the other coast and on to France. The sun was still shining and the Welsh roads weren't crowded. I was tuned to R.T.E. Radio, my last link with the old sod. This too would soon go as the transmitter went out of range, and I said prayers of another kind for he who never gave us a shortwave service.

The road through Anglesey wound its way through the valleys and here and there a hitch-hiker raised a thumb or held up a sign that said Birmingham or London. Wrapped up in my misery and the fading R.T.E. reception, I preferred the isolation and the company of my own thoughts to the risk of a boring passenger. My thoughts must have been elsewhere when I stopped and picked up a man of about thirty-five who sported a nice red nose and carried his possessions in a sack. "I'm going to London and on to Dover," I told him. "Ah great, I'm going to Southampton, I'll be with you almost to London, if that's alright with you." It was indeed, the Gods were with me, he was Irish, and right then that was all the credentials he needed.

From there on the clouds that darkened my personal sky began to drift a little. His name was Pat and he came from Kilkenny. For years he had worked the docks in England, wherever work was to be found. It wasn't by choice, but by necessity. There was nothing to do around his home place. But as we rolled off the miles of road it was quite obvious that his heart was very much back in Kilkenny. He missed the hurling and the lads around the village and the craic on a summer evening. He appreciated England, the land that gave him a living, and then he used a line that I've never forgotten, "I'm O.K., but I'm like a clock without hands, I'm ticking but I'm not showing the time." He hadn't been gathering much moss either, a rolling stone for sure, no wife, no base, and all he possessed in the world was in the sack on the back seat. Yet there was a depth and a magnetism about him that was greater than the worldly possessions he lacked. His mother was alive and lived alone at home, and every now and then he phoned her. "She's getting on now and I know she'd like me to be there, we talk now and then on the phone, but you know what really gets to me is I can always hear that old clock at home ticking away in the background."

We stopped at a roadhouse and had a meal and we were both in a mood to turn around and go back. We didn't, of course, and some hours and a hundred miles later, just west of London, we wished each other good luck and went our separate ways. As I pushed on across Europe and into the Middle East the journey was definitely the lighter for that chance meeting. I've given lifts to a good few hitch-hikers in my time, but Pat from Kilkenny left a little of himself behind. I remember being told once that "nothing is by chance or coincidence, even the briefest meeting has some significance." It's difficult to put a finger on the significance of that meeting, but I'm quite prepared to believe it had some.

— O —

A Time in Connemara

I T was Easter weekend and I was in Connemara. The first real holiday weekend of the year and with it came the first noticeable influx of tourists. Plenty of Dublin registrations and the odd French and German. The Americans were there too, that I could tell by the accents. For me Connemara starts at Maam Cross, the mountains start to gather in around you and that sense of being somewhere distant and different begins to grow. There can hardly be an Irish artist who ever took up a brush who didn't paint a scene from Connemara. I don't paint, although for a long time I've been saying, some day, perhaps. But I have tried to capture the magic of the place with my camera and whatever the composition, it is always the colour that dominates. That shade that lies somewhere between gold and brown, and which, like the name itself, belongs to nowhere but Connemara.

Anyhow, what I want to talk about is how a foreigner might see Ireland and on Easter weekend last how that visitor might have seen Connemara. For, as often as I have been in the place, it still had surprises for me. Out near Clifden there was this lake with a wooded island in the middle and a lovely backdrop of mountains, a real Paul Henry canvas. Such scenes are all over the place, but at that moment this one was lined up in my camera. An American had spotted the same scene and was doing likewise.

Now a few hundred yards back we had passed two donkeys on the road. They walked briskly and with purpose, they were not in the charge of anyone and they had all the appearance of animals, that short of having passports, were professional travellers. They came up to my car and the bigger of the two stuck his head in the window. At first I thought he was going to bite me. He wanted a bite alright, but not out of me. The American forgot about the Paul Henry scene, I could hear the buzz of his automatic, self winding camera as the two travelling asses sussed me out for grub. I had nothing to give them, so they wasted only about twenty seconds on me before heading for the American. Buzz went the camera and before you could say, Chicago, the big donkey was looking down the Americans throat. Mrs American must at some stage have had a fright on a safari in Kenya, for she dived into the car and wound up the window. The man produced an apple for each of the donkeys and now it was my turn to point the camera at him.

Many's the roll of film that's been spent on the great cathedrals of the world, Seville, Cologne, Rome and others. But on the road into Roundstone I watched and listened to two Germans as they photographed a small church. I don't speak a word of German, and I didn't need to, to know they were as excited as be-damned at what they had found. A small church huddled beneath a hill at a bend in the road. Atop a grassy mound stood a small bronze bell — I couldn't resist giving it a few gentle rings and listening to the faint echo drift across the valley. Beyond the mound the brown water of a full river rushed over the rocks, breaking what would otherwise be perfect silence. And again that river flowing away towards the stillness of the valley and the mountains beyond. It made me wonder what the fresh vision of a foreigner would be, not just of the mountains and the lakes and the colours, but things like the sheep and lambs that grazed by the roadside. A few upturned currachs, and two men cutting turf and speaking, as the song goes, "in a language that the stranger does not know."

At a filling station a Frenchman was trying to pronounce the placename, Toombeola, and I'm not even sure if that's how the natives say it. The road map he forgot to take from the roof of his car took off like a kite across the rocks and navigation is tough enough in Connemara even when the map stays with you. A mist made Roundstone appear out of the sea and at Dog's Bay another German photographed his own footprints in the white sand. On Easter Sunday morning, in the church that looks out over the sea above Roundstone, the priest preached one of the best sermons I've ever heard. He finished it off, by wishing us visitors safe home to our places in Ireland, or to wherever in the world we had come from on that Easter morning. I saw smiles on many of the foreign faces and I know they took back with them something of Connemara that no currency could buy.

— o —

The Alternative Concert

HE was watching me for a while and no doubt wondering "what the hell this old fogie was doing at a rock concert." His curiosity in me was temporarily as strong as his interest in the heavy sound coming from the stage. "Are you enjoying it?" he asked me. "It's fabulous!" I lied. Encouraged by my enthusiasm he offered me a swig from his plastic wine container. Ah well, in for a penny, in for a pound.

There's a lot of adjusting to be done by a person attending a rock concert whose youth was punctuated by ceili music and old time waltzes. But I discovered that there is for the youth of yesterday, as good a show off-stage, as there is on-stage for the modern devotee of rock. The day wasn't a very good day, it rained all morning, but the queue had been building from very early. By 10 a.m. it was a quarter mile long and five deep and the music was still two hours away and the rain still belted down. There wasn't a single pair of arms hanging idle, they were all engaged clutching to their chests large cider bottles and plastic wine packs. Along the entire line only two umbrellas were visible, all the hairstyles were alike, flat and dripping rain. A group of girls were getting a great laugh out of trying to get one of their friends into a black plastic bag. She was so wet already that the only thing she could have done in the plastic bag was germinate. Many of the arms, weary from hugging their booze, decided to lighten their load, they might as well be wet inside as outside.

The world of commerce arrived, two lads with baskets of sandwiches and a chap with three plastic bags full with coloured ribbons — I'm sure there's a proper name for the ribbons, but I don't know it. They bought them, well mostly, the girls did, then proceeded to tie them around their boyfriends' heads. I could only think of it as a sort of captured scalp ritual. Then it was eleven o'clock and the gates opened and they poured into the damp, empty arena and the first pecking order was established.

Those who would scream, shout and swoon at every sound and gyration were headed up front, they would stay there and they would be excited by everything. The more discriminating were picking their spots further back, where they could spread their ground sheets, or in under the stands for protection from the black clouds that still drifted across the sky at a pace.

It was eleven thirty but the big clock to the left of the stage showed seven twenty and the words emblazoned across the stage seemed like a hint to the clock, it read, 'Self-Aid Make It Work'.

Back at the gates they were pouring in and the queues were still growing. Word passed back along the line that the stewards were confiscating all booze at the gates and so they were; bins were being filled as rapid as unofficial dumps in the Dublin suburbs. The fans now decided to take in the cider and wine in the one way it couldn't be confiscated, inside their skins, — like the Jews at Massada, they would not be taken alive.

Mid-day and Brush Shiels came on-stage and had there been glass anywhere around it would surely have cracked from the roar. The volume from the stage sent shudders through the grass. A girl flung her jumper in the air and it drifted off in the breeze and the rain never to be seen by her again. Then surprise, surprise, I could make out the words and I was listening. I liked what I heard, Brush Shiels was singing about his dead friend, Phil Lynott, "Phil Old Pal" and reference to "the fishing boats at Howth" and for a while the oldest swinger at the concert was in tune with the youngest.

A young man who had somehow got through the outer defences with his cider bottle intact was sitting quietly by a fence quenching his thirst, when a defender of the inner circle spotted him, relieved him of the bottle, and before his very eyes poured the cider on the grass. The lad used neither a word nor jesture of protest, but he looked as sad as a man deserted by his bride on the wedding night. It was just about that time that the laws at the gate were being changed and they could bring in their booze.

The rain stopped and the sun, like a reluctant smiler, showed flashes of its teeth. Baked spuds were changing hands at 90p each as if a famine was imminent. A few who had come for Self-Aid were now in need of first-aid and had formed a queue at the ambulance station. Every toilet had a constant thirty yard queue, resigned and anxious faces indicative of its slow progress. It seemed as if the fans up-front were missing the rain, for stage-hands had now started pouring water over them and they accepted it as if it was the gift of life.

The evening drew in and the place was full — thirty thousand they say — Ann Doyle came on stage to present one of the groups. She remarked it was a change for her to see the audience. At that moment a lad standing near me didn't see any more of anything, he just folded up and fell over. It may have been the live Ann Doyle that did it, but I suspect it was the contents of the plastic bag that went down with him.

The music played-in the night and the lights came on and by now every fan was affected by the fever. My young nephew spotted me and thought it was a ghost, and couldn't wait to get home to tell his mother. Although we were both at the same venue we were enjoying different things. I would suggest you shouldn't close the lid on your youth until you've seen the alternative concert.

Clear Water

WE take it totally for granted. After all two thirds of the earth's surface is covered with it, ninety per cent of the body is made up of it, and it pours from the skies at the most inconvenient of times. Here in Ireland we don't even have to drill for it, just dam up a valley and let nature fill it. At least that's how it worked up to now. But the dry spells of recent years have lowered the levels of the reservoirs to where rationing has become necessary. An interesting side affect of this lowering of water levels has been, that every now and then during dry spells, the buildings that lie beneath the lake at Poulaphouca again appeared above the water line. At other reservoirs grass is again growing where millions of gallons of water once lay.

Around the year 1800 if someone said that very soon man would fly through the skies like a bird, and that in five hours he could get from here to New York, he would not have been believed. It would have been harder still to convince anyone that you could sit in your livingroom and watch a football match as it took place at that minute on the other side of the world. Back in the 1950's if I had told my grandparents that in a few years time every shop in the country would be selling water, and that it would cost nearly as much as beer, they would have said, 'the lad isn't right.' Mind you they had more appreciation for water than we have today. For starters they had a habit that modern medics recommend. First thing in the morning they drank a large glass of water. But their real appreciation possibly came from the fact that they had no water on tap, it had to be hauled in a bucket from the pump outside. In winter that pump had to be wrapped in straw to prevent it from freezing.

Washing machines were still mostly a thing of the future, and that was where the barrel that stood at the end of every rural house came in. It contained rain water, or as it was called, soft water. It was easier on the hands that were being worn out rubbing up and down on scrubbing boards. It was also better for washing the clothes. From this barrel came the water for everything except drinking. Despite the claims they make for the various bottled waters, I still feel that none of them can equal a drink taken straight from a spring well. This is water at its best, coming from deep within the earth. You look into the well and you see the water bubbling through the sand in the bottom.

Up it rises and then flows away gently through a stream. When you drink it, even on the hottest day, it is ice cool, and for a few moments it gives you a pain behind your eyes. Unfortunately today, with pollution from slurry, and excessive use of fertilisers, the number of healthy wells is being reduced. Often the modern farmer is the victim of his own or his neighbours excesses, when his own water supply becomes contaminated.

In Damascus it tends not to rain between April and October. Each year when the first rainfall came it was common to see the locals go out in the streets and dance about with their arms raised towards heaven in pure enjoyment at the return of the rain. It always amused me, I was more accustomed to seeing people throwing their hands to heaven in horror at the never ending rain.

Dublin uses around eighty-five million gallons of water per day. Did you ever wonder how they manage to keep it clean and healthy and how they know it is safe for drinking? In an age when man has sent spacecraft to the distant planets you'd imagine that technology could supply the best system. Not so, the technology is there, but it's a few trout swimming around enjoying themselves that give you an instant answer. If the trout are alive and well you may drink it.

Not alone does water feed the body, but it also feeds the soul. From the wonder of Victoria Falls and Niagara to the oceans of the world, their outstretched watery arms linking the continents. The sea is whatever you want it to be. Like man himself, a thing of many moods, from the angry storm tossed to the gentle waves that lap the shore. But I know a quiet place where a stream comes down from the mountain, tumbling over rocks and bending rushes in its path as it winds its way towards the valley. Cool, clear, fast flowing water, making its own music as it journeys onwards. This is my shrine to the God of water.

— O —

Death of a Racecourse

IT was like an American wake, they all came to celebrate, but behind the finery the smiles and the laughter it was still the death of the Phoenix Park Racecourse. On the day before a man in dress-ware and tall hat was standing at Doyle's Corner with a big placard that read, 'Last day at the Park tomorrow'. Shades of those who also carry notices predicting the end of the world — 'repent now, the end is nigh'.

Fifteen thousand souls turned up on the day, on another day half of that would have been a big crowd. The rains that had been filling the empty reservoirs outside Dublin halted and the sun lit up the tented village, the banners, the style, and the thousands of punters like myself who were there to be part of the history. A million pounds was at stake in the big race, the Cartier Million, but somehow it seemed secondary to the occasion as a whole. In the tented village the champagne flowed and all over the place well known faces dappled the scene like flashes of sunlight on a lake. The band played and the flag on top of the stand fluttered in the gentle breeze. The only real sign of death was in the trees where the autumn shedding of leaves had commenced.

A young man, whose memory of racing would barely stretch back to Lester Piggott's problem days, was telling an equally young lady how sad it was to see the end of eighty years of racing at the Park. The old fruit vendor, who for over sixty years had sold her wares inside the Park, now under the new system found herself outside the gate. Ironically the changes that were to be for the better seemed to work against the racecourse. The ordinary punters, the lifeblood of racing, didn't really feel at home here anymore, so they stayed away. But today they came back, by bike, bus and car, and at the same time every few minutes another helicopter dropped out of the sky. A man who was more interested in getting into tents than watching racing was complaining bitterly that too many places were out of bounds without a badge. I observed two other lads whom I'd swear were hell bent on souvenir hunting. They scanned with hawk like eyes anything that seemed capable of being moved, and even some things that didn't, like the winning post. And then the security men were shadowing them, their radio's crackling at their ears.

Just as the million pounder took off there was a temporary hush before the roar. For a few minutes the rich and not so rich were as one as the hooves of the cream of horseflesh reached out for the green turf.

111

Michael Kinane, on Rinka Das, led the twenty runners home and a fortune was lost and won. It was around half past five when Christy Roche passed the winning post on Wild Jester. The last race, the last winner for all time at the Phoenix Park. And I'll bet that in years to come that will come up in sporting questions.

It was all over including the shouting. Behind the scenes the stable lads were loading horses into boxes. A lad wearing a jockey's cap must have been there many times before, for he went back and had one last look at the racecourse. He was also thinking of Lester Piggott, for he remarked to another lad that "it was a pity Lester didn't make his comeback today." As it turned out Lester made his comeback a week later. It would have been ironic on the day; an old racecourse going and the old man of racing coming back.

The next sight of horses at the Phoenix Park Racecourse will probably be on the televisions in the houses that will stand where today the grass is still lush and green. If the ghosts of horses come back, the new house owners may sometimes hear the hammering of hooves at the midnight hour. Perhaps better that than the ghost of the man I saw ripping up his betting ticket and saying "may all me bad luck go with it." Some say there's a slim chance that racing may again return to the Park. But I feel that this is one Phoenix that will not rise from the ashes.

— O —

Words for the Weather

ONE wet day when I was very young an elderly neighbour of ours told me that they were about to build a roof over the country. My enthusiasm for the project was instantaneous, there would be no more wet days when we couldn't go out to play. Never for a moment was the idea considered impossible, the roof would go up and everyone would live happily ever after underneath it.

In a country like ours, even the children are caught-up with the weather, but what a pre-occupation we adults have with it. Of course it's not without good reason that we have to pay so much attention to the elements, but just look at the extent to which it has taken over our conversation. How often do you hear someone greet another with a simple "good morning" or "good evening?" You will of course, in most other places in the world, but not in Ireland. It's more likely to be "isn't it a lovely day" to which the other replies "It is indeed thank God", and then the note of pessimism "but will it hold?".

The greetings always contain a reference to the weather. Be it wet, miserable and windy, or mild, hot or roasting and a thousand variations in between. It's hard to decide whether we are paranoid about the weather or whether the subject gets us out of all kinds of awkward situations where we don't have anything to say, or else we don't know what to say. It can hardly be that we, the Irish, are stuck for something to say, after all we are one of the least tongue-tied nations in the world. We certainly have the gab, whether it's a gift or not.

I was a victim of the weather twice in my life so far. Years ago, miserable weather and worse pay drove me to the Middle East and beyond. It didn't take long until my rain sodden skull dried out. From there on the merciless sun burned the head off me, until eventually back I came to the land of the ever changing sky. A life time of habit is hard to change, regardless of how obvious the necessity may be. A certain Irishman who was senior in both position and age came out to work with us. He was assigned a secretary who came from an island much further east, a place that made the Middle East seem almost cool and damp. The only water her beautiful ebony coloured body came in contact with was in the bath. Every day our senior Irishman would arrive in his office and greet her with "isn't it a lovely day Miss Cardoza?" No doubt it was a lovely day, but so was the one before and a hundred before that and a further hundred after it,

113

and he had now been saying it for six months. Then one day Miss Cardoza came to me and asked, what does he mean 'isn't it a lovely day', don't we all know it's a lovely day, when is it not a lovely day?'' I spent a little time explaining to the dark skinned lady, from the lovely island, that there was another lovely island, far from her abode, where the sun didn't always shine, and that when it did we tended to talk a lot about it. Miss Cardoza said "Ah, I will understand in future.'' She didn't give our senior Irishman funny glances anymore in the morning, but I'm not convinced that she understood.

If Miss Cardoza ever comes to Ireland she won't know what has hit her. Not alone will we greet her with the weather of the moment, but we'll fill our conversation with her on the forecast as well. She'll be told "summer's finished, there's snow in that sky,'' or if perhaps the sun is shining, "that won't last, it's going to pour,'' even though there mightn't be a cloud between here and Mars.

In the city the greetings, in the main, are confined to the variations of temperature, the quantity of rain or the force of wind. In the rural areas they have an infinite variety on all this. A wet one becomes "no day for the hay,'' or if the clouds look ominous, "have you any hay down?'' "The river is rising'' means it has been raining heavy and still is, floods are imminent. "A hardy day'' is a very cold one, and a "soft day'' can be anything from mist to a deluge.

It's reasonable to assume that the seasons were planned in their infinite variety for our pleasure. In which case poor old winter seems to have fared badly. There are dozens of songs in praise of the other three, but I can't find many in praise of winter. Talking of winter, and cold ones,. I remember a man, Ger Hughes, long gone now. He was impressing on us kids how cold a particular winter of his youth had been. "It was so cold'' he said, "that talking to another man he could see the movement of his lips but could hear no sounds, not until the frozen words fell on the ground at his feet and smashed to pieces.''

By the way see if you can spend a day without mentioning the weather, and meanwhile cast an ear to see what others have to say about it.

— O —

114

The Attractions of Dublin

I F you must live in a city there can be few better places than Dublin. Although I must admit that for me, all else being equal, it will always be the pull of the wild. I can't help it, no more than I can help my height or the colour of my eyes. But the magic that sends something tingling through my soul is to be found in the mountains and in the woods and where the sun and shadow steal across fields of gold and green. And above all where the wild Atlantic lashes the remote and rugged coast of Ireland.

We tend to find ourselves where we are through force of circumstances. It's many a true son of the hills who now mows a little lawn behind a city house, while his heart is away on some great expanse of moorland with just himself and the lonesome call of a curlew.

If we could all deal our own hand of cards it would rarely be the one we were allotted. So, playing with what we got, those of us who were dealt Dublin didn't do too bad at all. When nature dressed the city she wasn't too stingy with her garments. On one side, standing like a great protector, the Dublin mountains and all along the other side the Irish sea lapping at its feet. Nature didn't stop there with her major architecture. She then drew a line right down the middle, and in from the plains of Kildare flowed a great river, the Liffey. The Vikings had an eye for a good place and to show they were ahead of their time when they built their settlement on the banks of the Liffey, they choose the site that a thousand years later Dublin Corporation would choose for its offices. The natives of later days built fine bridges and the north bank and the south bank were connected. The one named after a famous Kerryman was a godsend to many a lad from the provinces. You'd need to be bad not to find O'Connell Bridge.

This town was to be no London or New York, where the street is almost always in shadow and you seem to drive forever through an endless concrete jungle. Here the buildings don't kiss the clouds, but instead the person at the top window talks to the one in the street.

In Dublin the open space is never many minutes away and the sea is always there as the city follows its horseshoe shape around Dublin Bay. Of an evening take the road that rises sharply beyond Rathfarnham and there from the hills, when the sun goes down, watch the lights that twinkle from Dunlaoghaire to Lucan. A city pulsating with the life of a million souls.

Never a week passes that I don't spend some time in two of Dublin's finest parks, St. Anne's and the Phoenix Park. Where is there a city with seventeen hundred acres of parkland sitting just two miles from its centre? A place where you can sometimes be as alone as you might be on a Kerry mountain. Where a herd of deer eye you as if they had never seen a human before. Where waterhens break the silence as they scurry across a pond. Here all is peace and quiet and the world of nature is profuse in its presentations. Beyond the chestnut, the beech and the oak the river flows and the hum of the city seems a far distant thing.

St. Anne's park is a wonderland in miniature, open spaces, small clusters of trees and avenues lined with oaks. In springtime dappled with the gold of daffodils and in summer a rose garden that brings viewers from places afar. In winter the Brent Geese — all the way from the ice of Greenland — come to feed in its open spaces. They just hop across the road from the nature reserve on the Bull Island, another wonder of Dublin. Here, again within shouting distance of the city centre, can be found some rare species of birds. The sea laps around the island and offers them a safe home, while the rabbits and the hares burrow through the soft sand.

Unlike other cities where the parkland is tailored to its surroundings and is always dominated by the city, this is not the case with Dublin. The parks, in some form or other, were always there, so too the sea and the mountains. The people simply came and built their homes in between them and that's why today it all rests so easily together. A city where the generosity of nature makes the going easy for the natives and the ones from the hills alike.

— O —

Going Away

I T was deep winter and the weather was in keeping with the date. Rain, wind and bitter cold, an excellent day to leave Ireland, especially when the destination was Jerusalem. Today people are hopping around the world like ping pong balls, but in the sixties far away places were exactly that. The enthusiasm and ignorance of youth can be a curse, but more often it's a blessing, a sort of protective skin against the harsh realities. I should have been weighed down by the prospect of coping with a new life in a strange land, but I wasn't. There was also the consolation of company, a colleague was on the same assignment. The flight was via London, Zurich, Athens and Tel Aviv. We were like a pair of schoolboys, to raise the equivalent excitement today we would need to be travelling to the Moon, Mars and Jupiter.

On the London flight we met a newly ordained priest on his way to Nigeria. The poor man was in as bad a pickle as we were, he hadn't a clue what was in store for him either. From Zurich we mailed post cards and the same from Athens, we were rubber stamping the world, like little pups laying their marks on lamp-posts. What's seldom is wonderful and a practical experience beats a hundred tellings, it was hard to get it into our heads that above the cloudy skies of Ireland the sun always shone. But here we were riding along just above this ocean of cotton wool.

Reality was terra firma and we met it the moment we stepped on the tarmac in Tel Aviv. The telescopic tunnels that come up to aircraft doors weren't much in vogue in those days. You stepped onto the tarmac and either walked or bussed to the terminal building. Anyhow it was the blast of heat that deflated me. Back in Dublin it was possibly one or two degrees below zero and here it was maybe eighteen or nineteen above.

The road from Tel Aviv to Jerusalem climbs and winds through the hills. It was now nearing midnight and here and there the car lights picked out the remains of tanks and armoured cars, the remnants of battles, left there as shrines and propoganda. This was lesson two of the reality of the Middle East. Driving that night for the first time through the streets of Jerusalem I had expected to see and feel something special, but all I could see in the half light was the shuttered windows, street after street of grey shutters and grey walls, streets of flat roofed buildings, empty and silent, it could have been a ghost town.

Sleep didn't come easy that night, it was too hot. Next morning, my shoes, which the previous day had been soaked by Irish rain, stood with the toes curled up from the under-floor heating. Breakfast was a disaster, to this day remnants of the taste are jammed in my brain. The tea, the eggs, the bread, the milk, they all tasted horrible, the salt and sugar were the only recognisable things. You'd need to be starving to eat anything and two days later we were starving and we started to eat everything.

It was about that time that Larry made his apt statement, "here we are in the land where Christ was born and I wish to Christ we were back in the land where we were born." I was concurring with everything and outside in the harsh sunlight the white buildings reflected and the barren hills were bright and my eyes ran with the strain. My first purchase was a pair of sunglasses. Everywhere the sound of foreign language, dark skinned people, smaller in stature than the Irish. Orthodox Jews in their long black coats, black hats and long ringlets of hair touching their shoulders. Arabs looking like Lawrence of Arabia with flowing head-dress and baggy pants. We drifted through the scene as if it were a dream and sometimes we wondered if it was. That's how it all seemed in those first few days. Every lesson was learned the hard way. Only time would make this land a liveable place for the lads from the island in the far west.

— O —

A Glimpse of Syria

I F you look through the travel brochures you won't find many, in fact you may not find any, listing Syria among their destinations. What a pity, the loss is all to the traveller. Most likely that country wouldn't cross my mind either but for the fact that it was my home for four years.

My first glimpse of Syria was from the air. Having earlier flown over the fertile fields and the orange groves of Galilee, I was now looking down on the barren semi-desert. Then in the distance, Damascus. From the air it looked like an oasis in a wilderness. It gave me a sinking feeling, a sort of Alcatraz of the Middle East. It was all to be a pleasant surprise. Two years later when I could have left the country I opted to stay for a further two years. So much for first impressions.

Syria is an old country, six thousand years ago settlements existed near Damascus. Numerous civilisations came and conquered and were in turn conquered themselves, leaving Damascus the tantalising mixture it is, one of the world's great living museums of the history of man. It is also a land of friendly and hospitable people with a long history through a myriad of cultures.

Living in Damascus took a lot of getting used to. Going down to the market each day for the groceries. Shopping in a street that was built by the Romans two thousand years ago. At the end of the street a stone arch and high above it the window from which Saint Paul was lowered in a basket to escape his pursuers. Here the hardware and the grocer and the shoe shop do not stand side by side but rather a whole area is given over to one type of business, thus all the grocers are together and all the shoe shops and so on.

Ali Hussein kept me in bread for four years and he drove me out into the desert to see the ruined city of Palmyra. Perhaps the finest example in the world of a Roman city, the setting sun casting long shadows from the one hundred and fifty or so columns that still stand. The remains of temples and shops, and the pedestals on which statues once stood, some of the statues still lying where they fell. A whole city scattered in the sand. The great Temple of Bel dominated the city and the empty echoing spaces of its courtyard sent soundwaves across the centuries.

We went down to the Euphrates and followed the old road the Romans built from the great river across the desert to the Mediterranean. With typical Roman thoroughness they dug wells every twenty four miles,

The Great Mosque at Damascus.

regardless of how deep they had to dig. The caravans were protected by patrols of the Roman Camel Corps. Each year during the holy season of Ramadan I watched the caravans of the twentieth century passing through Damascus. Thousands of battered buses and cars making the pilgrimage to Mecca. Gone were the days when the great trades converged on Damascus, the incense routes of Arabia and the silk traffic from China. These poor pilgrims would only fill their water cans and head back out into the desert. Some prayed at the great Ommayad Mosque, considered the most interesting Islamic building in the world, it ranks after Mecca, Medinah and the Dome of the Rock in Jerusalem as the holiest place on earth.

Along the Barada river the road led to Jerusalem, through the poplars and past the shrine marking the spot where St. Paul was knocked from his horse on his way into the city. In the distance Mount Hermon, the grey haired mountain, its peak constantly covered in snow. On that same road one morning I saw the remains of a village, a heap of stones and twisted steel and fragments of furniture, and women crying while the smoke still rose from the ruins. An hour earlier it had been a living village, and then the war-planes came.

But in the midst of disaster life went on, and in the suk, Cha Cha sold hand carved copper veined with silver and brass. On that collonaded street, where the chariots once ran, today's traders display lengths of the rich Damask brocade. Sacks of dried apricots and shelled walnuts perfume the air, together with the strong smell of Turkish coffee. The pace of life is easy. Damascenes say that "Hurry is written on the hoof of a donkey."

The Romans came and went. Today the evidence of different ages lie piled on each other. In a factory the top of a Roman pillar protrudes through the floor, an electric light switch fastened to it. The Damascenes took the Romans' gold but refused their culture. Damascus markets are sadder than most because their beauty has degenerated rather than vanished. Syria is a country with its own magic, still mostly unknown to the modern traveller. Damascus is also a town of modern buildings where the Bedouin and his camel come to trade and then disappear into the distance where the desert and the sky burn into each other.

My landlady in Damascus was a Christian and she came from a village called Maloula. I had never heard of the place, even though there was, and is, every reason why it should be famous.

My first visit to Maloula was on a lovely autumn day. It's about 45 miles from Damascus and on the way we would visit Seidnaya. At first the landscape was barren and treeless, almost desert-like after the long hot days of summer. Near the village a stream flowed and there was a hint of vegetation. A small group of women were beating little bundles of wheat with flails, as their ancestors might have done two thousand years before.

121

The Greek Orthodox convent of Seidnaya, on a rock, towered over the village. A building of white bricks topped by a clock tower and a dome of faded silver. Having climbed a maze of zigzagging steps, I entered the fourteen hundred year old convent through a low doorway. The convent's treasure lies at the back of the altar. A pair of silver doors open to show an iron grille, and behind that grille lies a silver casket. It is said that the casket contains the first picture of the Virgin and Child, painted by Saint Luke the Evangelist. Others claim that the original painting was stolen by the Crusaders and taken to Rome. Travellers of long ago wrote that the picture had only traces of paint on it, having been worn away by the kisses and caresses of pilgrims. A strange thing about the convent is that it isn't only a place of Christian pilgrimage. Moslems flock there in their thousands, and every year many miraculous cures are reported. They say that if all the people cured there over the centuries were lined up they would stretch back to Damascus.

At Maloula the entrance to the village is a gravel road lined with tall poplars. A stream of fresh water flows down from the rocks, following the road and disappearing into the sparse vegetation beyond. The village is set into rock. Row upon row of houses climbing over each other. At the top the rock splits and you walk through a gorge a quarter of a mile long and at some points only a yard wide. Sitting on the rock I was looking down on the village below and at the convent of Saint Tekla. Legend says that Saint Tekla was a disciple of Saint Paul and that for her belief she was pursued by her pagan father and at Maloula the mountain opened to allow her to escape. The same passage I had just walked through.

When the sun went behind the rock long shadows were cast across the village and the proprietor of the coffee shop placed small stools outside the door. We sat in the cool shade drinking cups of that very strong coffee that is common to the Arab world. "It was once an all Christian village," he told me. "It is now half Christian and half Moslem." The men drinking their coffee across from us were not speaking in Arabic, therefore it had to be Aramaic. "Yes" the coffee shop man said, "we always speak Aramaic here, it is the last village in Syria to use the language." And he added, "you know it was the language spoken by Jesus?" I did indeed know, in fact it was the reason for my visit to Maloula. It was the language of the Persian Empire and five hundred years before Christ it was spoken all over the Middle East. To-day, Maloula is the last bastion of that ancient tongue. It was dark as I left Maloula and rows of lights shone from the open doorways of the tiers of houses. Night was closing in on the last custodians of the language of Christ. A village out of time, in a country that has so much to offer when it opens its doors to the world.

Saint Patrick's Day Overseas

NATIONAL Day celebrations at home bear no resemblance to the variety of ways it is celebrated by the Irish in foreign lands. The city of New York is taken over by the Irish on St. Patrick's Day. Jamaicans and Chinese, all sporting green faces, Irish for a day. Here in Ireland the feeling isn't the same. It's all here, one is part of the whole, both actor and audience at once. That real sense of, 'Ireland my country', is the privilege of the emigrant. Maybe it's the "far away hills are green" syndrome, but it certainly sharpens the feeling of belonging to a people and a place.

Many a Saint Patrick's Day I spent far from Ireland. It was never in the sophistication of the United States, or anywhere amongst great numbers of fellow Irishmen. Apart from one each, in Cyprus, India and Pakistan, most of the Saint Patrick's Days I spent away from home were in the Middle East. Just a handful of kindred souls, scattered amongst the diversity of nationalities working for the United Nations. A handful of people with an extraordinary need for self identification, a need we amply fulfilled on our National Day.

The one I like best to remember was spent in Jerusalem. Preparations started months in advance. It was customary that each nationality, on their national day, would give a party for the others. The Canadians and Italians were good at it, but the Irish were the best. Proof of this was the numbers who turned up. We had Guinness shipped from Ireland, and a man from Kenya said, "the black drink made him feel at home." He missed the punch in the Irish jokes that were being told, but he laughed heartily at the line in a song that went "they had to tear the paper off the wall to make room for all the people in the hall." The hall that night was indeed full, and we sported sprigs of half dead shamrock, that had survived a flight from Dublin.

The day started with a Mass. We had an Irish priest for the occasion, and had he known what we had in mind for the afternoon, he would surely have given us the last rites. The tradition of the Railway Cup matches in Croke Park must have been our inspiration. We arranged a Gaelic Football game. The Irish would play the rest. We simplified it for the newcomers, catch it, kick it, and don't kill anyone. The Swedes, Danes, Dutch and a dozen other nationalities, had come along fine in pre match practice. We were only nine Irish, so, weeks in advance, we selected six sportingly adaptable Arabs and made them honorary Irishmen.

Our pitch was a dusty piece of level ground on top of a hill overlooking Jerusalem. A tricolour was hoisted and the fray was on. I'm not sure who won that day, but I certainly remember the match. Unaccustomed as they were to Gaelic Football, the converts to the code took to the game with a diligence that should have brought them to the top in any field of endeavour. This had all the flavour of Junior Club football in rural Ireland, with its attendant risks, the only difference was the field of battle. Eventually a truce was called, the tricolour was lowered and the weary troops went away to wash their wounds and prepared for the evening's revelry. Somewhere still, in far flung corners of the world, there are men who recall the day they played "Irish Football". And Saint Patrick will have looked down on us with a quare ould smile on his face. For in our hearts we will have been back in Ireland, with the parade in O'Connell Street, or the crowd at Croke Park, or a thousand other places of personal memories.

The party started as the sun went down on the old city of Jerusalem. Song and dance and liquid beverage flowed, the wounds from the football match were forgotten. A bottle of poteen was passed around, and a Dutchman, who had suffered a swollen limb in the match, was advised to rub some of it on his injury. He tasted it first, and discovered that it was a better pain reliever when "rubbed in" from the inside.

There's an expression, "He'd sell sand to an Arab," and that night I saw a man do it. An Irish Army Commandant, who shall remain nameless, so as to protect the guilty, hit on a rather brilliant idea. He got a helmet — there was no scarcity of them — he deposited into it the remnants of every drink he could find. He took his 'helmet cocktail' and stood at the top of the room and announced to the assembled that it was a concoction of ancient origin which had been passed down to him through his family, that it was a cure for everything, and guaranteed virility. He solemnly told them it would only work when made and drunk on St. Patrick's Day. He almost had the hands bitten off him from mouths trying to get into the helmet.

The remarkable thing was that no one said they felt the worst for having supped from his helmet, in fact he was getting compliments for months afterwards. The night ended, we played our national anthem and felt a sense of Irishness that you can only feel when far away from home. That night, from Kenya to Kentucky, Ireland made many new friends and the Irish tourist board never knew the great work that was accidentally being done by a handful of emigrants.

— O —

Coming Home for Christmas

I T was a few weeks before Christmas when I bumped into an old friend. As we parted I invited him to call to the house over the holiday. "Ah, I'd love to, but we're off to the Canaries." It's the new trend, the turkey isn't the only thing to get brown at Christmas. It seems as if there is always a great wanting to be where we're not.

Many is the Christmas Day I spent in places where the only clue to the day that was in it, was the calendar showing December 25th. One year it was on the banks of the Suez Canal. It was a hot day and we tried to eat a bird that was masquerading as a turkey and it was so tough that not even one of the mines that the Egyptians had planted near our building would have torn the thing apart. We were about twenty in numbers that day, all men and from almost as many countries. We played poker, drank beer and in quiet moments made our flights of fantasy to places as far apart as Copenhagen, Sydney and Dublin. It was blessed relief when the day was over, for we knew that back home it was over also, and that next year we might spend it in Ireland.

That brings me to Damascus and the day before Christmas Eve and my friend and colleague, Ben Bengtsson from Sweden driving me to the airport on my way to Ireland. Like the taste of something fine, I can still savour the joy of it. There was a very sad note also, although little did either of us know it that warm December morning, but before I would get back to Damascus Ben would be dead, killed in a road accident in Lebanon, at twenty nine years of age. However, that morning disaster was far from our minds. We crossed the city and drove down Abou Roumanie, the O'Connell Street of Damascus. Not a hint of Christmas in the air. The leaves on the trees, the sun bright and warm and the traders busy selling their wares in the streets. One small exception, the only supermarket in town, Nooradins Grocery, which had all the custom of the foreign population, had a tiny Christmas tree stuck in the window in the midst of corn flakes and cans of dried milk.

Getting on the plane in my shirt sleeves, but with a heavy coat on my arm which I knew I would need before the sunset of that day. The temperature dropped at every stop, Athens, Rome, London. It was dark on a crisp frosty evening as we descended to Dublin. You can't understand the pure joy of it unless you've been long and far away and when you have it's easy.

The lights of Dublin winking below you, then you can see the traffic on the Swords Road, lights going towards the city and others towards their homes in the suburbs. Very soon you'll be down there and one of them. Family and friends will be there and there'll be hugs and smiles and warm handshakes and the odd tear of joy. You listen to the sound of your footsteps on the ground and the sound is music to your ears, for it's your land, it's Christmas and you're home.

The next day, Christmas Eve, I went into Dublin, shivering slightly and still trying to adjust to the cooler air. But here in O'Connell Street the world was alive. This was no Abour Roumanie, with its one Christmas tree amidst corn flakes and dried milk. Lights everywhere, and a hundred trees in a hundred windows and one mighty big one where Nelson used to stand. Everywhere carol singers and the jingle of coins in boxes and buckets. People laden down with parcels, good humouredly trying to squeeze through the crowds, and me, like a ghost, drifting through it all. Not knowing anyone and meeting no-one that knew me, yet all around me was everything that was part of me. The street trader in Moore Street offered me crackers and I bought some even though I didn't want them, then she wished me a Happy Christmas and it was the first person who had spoken to me. Every now and then I'd wonder for a few seconds if perhaps it was all a dream and I'd wake up in Damascus.

I went into a pub and the buzz from the streets was still there. Full to the doors, the tinkle of glasses, the smiling faces, the exchange of greetings, the warm air and the lot of them half way to total merriment. I found a place and sipped and savoured. Sitting on the top deck of the bus going home to the suburbs that evening I spotted lighted Christmas candles in windows. A drunk fell off the seat opposite me and I knew I wasn't dreaming and I was quite happy. I was sure of something else too. The pain of being far away is worth it for the sheer joy of coming home for Christmas.

— O —

Kashmir

DRIVING for twelve hours along torturous roads, twice detouring to avoid landslides, I was tired and hungry and my skull throbbed with a headache. For the last hour the car had been climbing steadily and was now at 8,000 feet. I had arrived. This was the Banihal Pass in northern India, gateway to the plains of Kashmir. Suddenly the aching head and the empty stomach were forgotten, I had never seen anything like the view before me. Far behind lay the hot dusty roads and the teeming cities of India, ahead and far below was the verdant Vale of Kashmir, set against the frozen splendour of the Himalayan ramparts.

The waterways that ran like veins through the green valley dazzled in the setting sun. On one side the Pir Panjals reached up to 16,000 feet, and guarding the northern side were the world's highest mountains, the Himalayas. Down in the valley farmers worked teams of oxen pulling wooden ploughs as their ancestors had done for centuries. Barefooted children and young women herded flocks of mountain goats. Civilisation had not touched this Eden of Asia. And yet I was coming here because of war; three times India and Pakistan went to war over the territory, and then, as now, a United Nations Peace Keeping Force was maintaining a cease-fire line between them.

Srinagar, the state's capital, is halfway up the valley. A town of rivers and canals, the houses are suggestive of Alpine chalets, built of sun-baked brick with wooden trimmings and thatched roofs. The waters of Dal lake form the northern edge of the town. Here were the houseboats, some six hundred of them, flat bottomed boats that serve as both transport and habitation. They ranged from humble tubs to floating palaces, some up to one hundred and forty feet long and containing elaborate furniture.

The big boats rarely leave their moorings, instead people paddle across the water in shikaras — boats resembling gondolas — fitted out with gaily patterned cushions. These boats also serve as water taxis, and for a few rupees they will take you for hours through the wonderland of waterways and floating gardens.

Shopping in Srinagar was a unique experience. The Bazaars, mostly of hole-in-the-wall type shops, offering a dazzling array of eastern treasures, fine jewellery, precious stones, and what I found most attractive, beautiful wood carvings. The Kashmiris have a reputation for sharp dealing, and the sleepy-eyed merchant puffing at his 'hubble bubble' — the ever present water-pipe — is not in business for charity. This I found out when I bought a lovely aquamarine stone from a travelling trader. I had the stone examined, it was glass, the aquamarine was gone, and so was the trader. I don't know where some of the stores got their names, and I wouldn't care to comment on the appropriateness of the names of their proprietors — there was Cheap John, Subhana the Worst and Suffering Moses.

The Mogul emperors dedicated themselves to opulence, they built fabulous pleasure gardens on the outskirts of Srinagar; their personal versions of paradise are fine examples of elegance and extravagance. The most famous of the gardens is Shalimar, which means 'abode of love'. Traversed by rivulets and plumed with fountains, Shalimar is laid out in four broad terraces, rising towards wooded hills. In marble pavilions, royalty and guests could play and dine amid the splashing water and the whispering trees. I felt transported back in time, dreaming the dreams of kings, and then went back to the town and called on the priest, Father Joe Jones from Cork, and we shared an Indian curry.

It was now April and the snow was creeping back into the mountains when I got to Gulmarg, 'the meadow of flowers'. At 10,000 feet it is a green clearing in the mountain. Quaint cottages recall the time when British officers came here with their families from the Punjab to dance the summer nights away or to hunt the snow leopard and the Himalayan bear. I did none of these things, but I did see Nanga Perbat, 'the naked goddess' the 26,620 foot peak of the Himalayas acclaimed by many as the most beautiful mountain in the world.

The magic of the hills pulled me on and into Ladakh, the one free corner of Tibet. The Ladakhis are a cheerful people, they speak a dialect of Tibetan and practice lamaism. I saw nomads from the far plains taking their flocks to summer pastures and caught sight of a herd of yaks grazing in a field of mountain wild flowers. My feeling was of being at the top of the world, then the road ended, and beyond that barrier was "no go" land, Chinese territory. The day I left Kashmir I flew to Agra to see the Taj Mahal. The sight of the Taj Mahal was stunning, but somehow my heart was back, where a little of it will always remain, in the cool, clean air, in the mountains of Kashmir.

— O —

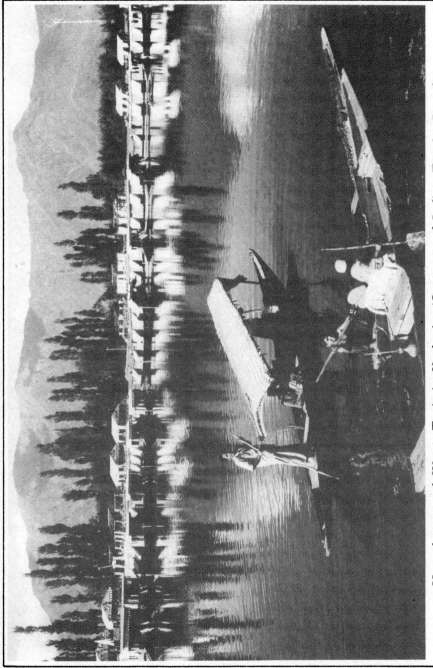

Houseboats and Water Taxis in Kashmir. (Courtesy of Indian Tourist Board).

The Amphitheatre at Jerash.

The Ancient City of Jerash

THE planes that catapult travellers into the skies, to place them down at the tourist watering holes of the world, off-load few of their passengers in Jordan nowadays. Since Israel occupied the West Bank of the River Jordan and took control of perhaps the most valuable tourist attractions in the world, namely, Jerusalem, Bethlehem and to a lesser extend Jericho, Jordan has become a ghost land where tourism is concerned and what a pity. It's still worth travelling half way round the world, if only to see the ancient ruins of Jerash, not to mention the hidden city of Petra, which must surely rate as one of the wonders of the world.

Jordan is one vast open-air museum. Since the first light of civilization, peoples, nations and invading armies have dwelt in, marched across, and devastated this ancient land. All left traces of their passage.

Jerash, the city that ranks with Baalbek and Pompeii, lies in a well watered valley thirty miles north of Amman, the Jordanian capital. The desert sands of centuries blew across the valley, until only the tops of a few columns were visible above the brown dust. Then in 1806 a German Archaeologist named Seetzen started to dig and he soon realised that here lay the relics of an ancient civilisation. When the Romans erected their beautifully architectured city they obliterated many signs of previous inhabitants. But compared to the evidence found the Roman era seems almost modern. Flint instruments found date Neolithic Jerash to about 6,000 B.C., while outside the walls lay the remains of a Bronze Age settlement of around 2,500 B.C. All this makes Wood Quay seem like it hasn't happened yet.

The Jerash I saw, almost in its entirety, was the city of the Romans. No town-planner today will leave behind what their Roman predecessor did, no bewildering maze of haphazard streets, nor the monotonous geometrical designs of modern cities. I first went there on a spring day when the winter rains had given life to vividly coloured flowers that crept out between the ancient stones. The street of columns — the city's main street — starts at the Triumphal Arch, which was built to commemorate the Emperor Hadrian's visit around 129 A.D. Just inside the Arch, which is a triple gateway about 40 feet high and 85 feet wide, is the great Oval Forum, which is also colonnaded. This was the place of public meetings, civic affairs and the market.

There were also three Roman theatres and a huge stadium used for chariot racing or gladiatorial sports. To this day the remains of goal posts used for polo can still be seen. The street intersections were marked by traffic towers, topped with statues.

The evening sun cast long shadows from the variety of tall Ionic and Corinthian columns that marked the changing fashions in architecture over the centuries. For a sense of contact with the past I walked barefooted along the paved street laid by Roman hands and thought on the sandalled feet that walked these same stones so many centuries ago. All along the colonnaded street lie the remains of shops, temples and fountains. High above the city stood the Temple of Artemis, its magnificent columns pointing skywards, like great stone sentries of a bye-gone age. It must have been a magnificent sight with its red tiled roof, elaborate carvings and marble statuary.

Everywhere in the paved street were deep ruts caused by chariot wheels. Several times I sat on the stones and ran my fingers through the markings. I thought of Ben Hur and so real for me was the sense of time reversal, that looking around me, it seemed it would not be strange that this ancient transport would come thundering along.

The south theatre is in superb condition. The porticoed entrances on each side of the large stage are intact. Walking across the stage my footsteps echoed up and away through the tiers of stone seats on which the Romans had sat all those centuries ago. Perfect acoustics from long before the birth of amplification. The ghosts of actors and audience must leave traces of their existence in the stones, for it isn't hard to imagine the scene as it must have been.

Near the city gate a large pool was uncovered, nearly two hundred yards long and very deep, this was used for large scale boat battles and other water sports. The West Baths were used as an exclusive club by wealthy Romans, it was the setting for lavish parties and aquasports. Such affluence measured against the period it was happening in must surely remain unequalled today.

Jerash died a lingering death, the cancer of invasion and earth-quakes took their toll and between the eighth and the twelfth centuries, this once noble city, slipped, like an old wino, into a semi-conscious state. The Crusaders came and found her thus. They had no appreciation for her treasurers or architectural wonders. They stabled their horses in its noble buildings and turned the Temple of Artemis into a garrison and thereby sounded the death knell for the beautiful city of Jerash.

— O —

Stranded in Italy

T HE Middle East was in turmoil, in particular Lebanon, and once again war was eating away at the heart of Beirut. That's what was causing problems for me. Two months earlier when I drove my car onto a ship in the Port of Beirut and headed for Naples things were peaceful. Brown bodies swam in the warm, blue mediterranean and tourists sipped cool drinks in the outdoor cafés along the Al-Hamra. Now, two months later, the cafés were bombed to oblivion and the only thing to be found on the beaches of Beirut was unexploded shells.

The ship to take me back was to sail from the Adriatic Port of Brindisi. The holidays were over, the money was spent and driving down the crowded roads of France and Italy in the heat of mid-summer was far removed from the quiet lanes and the cool air left behind in Ireland. In Rimini it was hot enough to fry eggs on the pavement, and along the beach endless rows of striped bathing huts and everywhere anthills of bronzed bodies. But there wasn't time to pause and enjoy it, I had to push on.

The office of the Adriatica Shipping Line in Brindisi was a scene straight from Casablanca. In the ceiling big cartwheel fans spun lazily, while the staff at the desks beneath operated to the same rhythm. In the frustration of trying to make myself understood I thought, 'Oh God, if only Esperanto had caught on'. When you want urgent information there can be little that's more frustrating than two people talking to each other in different languages. He threw his hands in the air and I threw my hands in the air and only the hum of the lazy fan broke the silence. Then he had an idea, he smiled and disappeared through a door. It was the kind of smile that says, hold on, you're mad and I'm going for the police. He was back in a minute another smiler in tow. Smiler number two was learning 'Engleasie', he had once been to London for a week. "It was a lo-o-vely place", "did I know London?" Sure I did, but what about the ship to Beirut? "Ah Senor, it e-es cancelled, the Kap-i-tan will not sail to Beirut in de war." But, smiler continued, "perhaps another she-e-p from Napoli in ten days!"

Back in the street I was sweating from more than the sun. The funds were low, Naples was over two hundred miles away on the other coast and maybe, just maybe, in ten days time, there would be a ship. The extreme south of Italy is as sparsely populated as Connemara. It is close to the Mafia homeland of Sicily and in the small towns you get the feeling the stranger sticks out like a lighthouse beacon. In the town of Potenza the rented room was basic and in keeping with the diet of bread, milk and cheese, which I bought in the shop next door. If there was no ship in Naples the following week the funds would have to meet an extended seige.

A colourful procession moved through the town and I walked along with it, anything to pass the time. On a small concrete patch beside the church a group of young lads played football with the fervour of a World Cup. I sat on the steps of a monument and watched them and it was a World Cup. It's amazing how engrossed you can become in almost nothing when your range is narrowed.

Back at the rented room the landlady smiled. The shopkeeper smiled as I bought more cheese and bread. The lads sitting at the base of the monument smiled and offered me a seat every time I came to look at the football. I began to wonder what it would be like to actually talk to someone again. After six days of no words and many smiles I vacated my place on the monument steps and headed for Naples.

Naples is an exciting city, but not a place to drop your guard. The foolhardy leave the town as naked as plucked chickens. In the harbour two aircraft carriers of the American Sixth Fleet lay at anchor and at every turn of every street one could see American sailors. Checking to see if I still remembered how to speak English, I bumped into one of them. A lad from Kentucky, who seemed to have more affinity with the blue grass country than the ocean waves. In the biggest pub I've ever seen, an U.S. Navy establishment called the 'Blue Angel' we drank American beer with about two thousand others. The lad from Kentucky told me how he wanted to go back to being a school-teacher and I gave him a hundred reasons why he should visit Ireland.

My ship came in and the day we sailed I got a great bargain in a brand-name watch. As we sailed out of the Bay of Naples, with Sorrento on one side and the Isle of Capri on the other, passing us at close range and in contrast to the tranquil surroundings, was one of the U.S. carriers. On deck a group of sailors waved and I wondered if one of them was the lad from Kentucky. A week later in Beirut the guns were temporarily silent and the watch I bought in Naples was as silent to my ears as the bells of Christchurch, two thousand miles away in Dublin. Which goes to prove that Naples is not the town for innocents abroad.

— O —

A Time at the Suez Canal

T HE Suez Canel, connecting the Mediterranean and the Red Sea, is perhaps the most valuable stretch of water on this planet. Nowadays, 25,000 ships per year pass through the canal between the cities of Port Said and Suez, earning for the Egyptian Government around £1,500 million a year. For shippers, time is money and a ship using the canal, say between London and Bombay, shortens the distance by around 12,000 miles. One of the most sophisticated navigational guidance systems in the world controls all shipping in the canal and for 22 miles out to sea at each end. The authority operating it employs 15,000 people and perhaps as much as ten per cent of the world's seaborne trade passes through the Suez Canal. It's a busy place and a profitable business for all concerned.

There was a time when it wasn't so busy, in fact it wasn't in use at all, save for the dolphins that went playfully and in peace up and down the famous waterway. The six day war in 1967 saw the Israeli Army advance through Gaza and the Sinai Desert and stopping at the Suez Canal. Ships, unlucky enough to be using the canal when the war started, were bombed and sunk. One ship was stranded in mid-canal and spent the next eight years waiting to be released. Immediately after the first round of war, when a cease-fire came, a United Nations peacekeeping mission went in to monitor events. Like the stranded ship, they too stayed until Anwar Sadat made peace with Israel, and the canal reopened in 1975.

I was part of that first group that went in and established a base at Ismalia on the Egyptian side. In a war situation, in spite of what is said, there really is no book of rules. Survival is paramount and you write the rules as you go along. We arrived in the almost deserted and partly destroyed town with a few white jeeps and a bag of money. First task was to have a look around and find a suitable place to set up house. Right smack on the canal bank was a lovely villa that had survived the war. Nasser had once used it as a summer residence. It was very suitable for our purposes and the Egyptian authorities agreed we could use it. First priority was to build a radio mast, we needed communications with our bases in Cairo and Jerusalem and on to New York. Help was hired locally, wherever we could find it. Carpenters, mechanics, cooks. The bag of money was getting lighter. There wasn't must use flashing cheques, the nearest bank was in Cairo. It was mercilessly hot, and if that wasn't bad enough they started to shoot at each other. Out came the bag of money again, we needed men to build a bomb shelter. Twenty yards from the villa they built it, in the middle of the nice garden. A layer of planks and a layer of sandbags, and another layer of planks and sandbags. It would withstand anything except a direct hit with something heavy. Next thing was to practise at getting into it fast when shooting started. Beside the villa stood a mosque. Very soon the Israelis shot a few feet off the top of it. Peace for a few days and then another exchange of fire, and when we came from the shelter the mosque was shorter still. The winter set in, it was as warm as a good Irish summer, and the warring parties exchanged prisoners. Red Cross boats ferried them across the canal. They weren't showing any trust in each other, so the boats left opposite sides of the canal simultaneously. The dolphins swam playfully beside them.

Every few weeks we backed off for a couple of days and went up to Cairo. We marvelled at the Pyramids, and went down and dipped our toes in the Nile and watched the Arab dhows with their black sails glide gently by. And you mustn't forget your malaria pills each Saturday, or as one Irishman put it, "if you do you'll be leppin' and sweatin' all over Connemara for the next thirty years."

We were living between the two front lines and it wasn't always the most comfortable of places. When they weren't shooting at each other, the Israelis and the Egyptians tended to shout abuse across the couple of hundred yards that divided them. This would often go on in the middle of the night, possibly scared soldiers trying to relieve their nervousness. It wasn't helping our nerves either, not to mention our sleep. Just for variety every now and then one side or the other would fire flares, turning the midnight sky into a blaze of light and exposing any movement that might be taking place. Often it was the signal to get your head down. For several years that pattern was maintained, with a few pauses for major hostilities. During one big fight the United Nations building was left like the temple of old, not a stone upon a stone, other than in a big heap of course. Most of us had a philosophy that if your number isn't up you needn't worry. Meanwhile the dolphins became more numerous and the white sands of the Sinai Desert silted the Suez Canal. And the ships sailing from London to Bombay travelled an extra 12,000 miles.

— o —

136

A Christmas in the Holy Land

MY first Christmas away from Ireland was spent where it all began, the Holy Land. It's not a place you find too much bad weather, even in winter. No blanket of snow to make the postcard scene, and little of the Western atmosphere that raises the lowest of spirits. Few Christmas trees winking from livingroom corners and yet, this place is the heart of it all.

Living in Jerusalem, Bethlehem was just a few miles down the road. Around ten o'clock on Christmas Eve night I joined the throng that was filling the narrow winding road joining the two towns. I had no ticket to get inside the church, so that left me standing in Manger Square with what seemed like a million others. It sounded like the Tower of Babel, every language under the sun was being spoken. Lighted candles flickered in the cool night air while loudspeakers relayed the ceremonies from inside the church. At midnight the bells rang out and the crowds, for whom there was no room within, knelt in the streets, and over the whole scene a clear and starry sky. Watching the stars I almost expected one to drop from the heavens and hover over the church.

Bethlehem is sheep country and making our way downhill and out of the town we could hear the sheep bells clanging and the irritated shouts of shepherds awakened from their slumbers by the nocturnal visitors. John McFadden, another exile far removed from his native Donegel, was intent on not letting me get homesick. Picking me up in the early afternoon on Christmas Day, he announced, "There's a few things I want to show you, aye, and if you have a swimming trunks bring it".

We took the road from Jerusalem that winds and drops all the way down to Jericho. The barren hills looked like a moonscape. Thirty miles and three quarters of an hour or so later I was having my photograph taken beside a monument which said I was standing at the lowest spot on earth. Twelve hundred feet below sea level. From Jerusalem we had dropped three thousand seven hundred feet and the temperature was pleasant in the mid seventies. Right behind us the Dead Sea lapped gently on a pebble beach. "Whatever you do don't swallow the water and don't get it in your eyes," John shouted after me as I walked into the Dead Sea.

I walked out to chest height and then I popped up like a cork. The salt concentration in the water is so high that it isn't possible to sink. I wondered about a walking trick. That wasn't really on, but it was possible to sit there as if in the most comfortable of reclining chairs.

Overlooking the sea was the Epsom of the desert. No Turf Club here, but certainly a good 'Sand Club'. Painted barrels buried in the sand marked out the circular track. Big raw boned camels snapped at each other and anyone that came within range. Owners with mean faces flung frightened looking jockeys aloft, eventually they were off, in a most uneven start. I had my few pennies on the one that was faced the wrong way when the flag was dropped. Three times around the barrels they went, with long looping strides that looked like slow motion. My fellow picked up a few places, but not enough to get him in the frame. The one that came in last was in real trouble, before he got to the finish line, the jockey, his big polka-dot shirt blowing around his head like a parachute, jumped to the sand and took off as fast as his short legs would carry him. He disappeared over a dune with about twenty angry punters in close pursuit. It seems as if his camel was a good one, but the reward for losing was greater than for winning. It was obvious that for a punter to make money it was necessary to know more about the jockey than the camel.

In Jericho town tall date trees lined the streets, behind old-world shop fronts traders sat sleepily, their wares in front of them, inviting the little custom that was around. The few vehicles that moved raised clouds of dust that settled on everything. It was sunny and hot, we sat on low stools beneath the shade of a tree and drank fresh orange juice. It wasn't the kind of Christmas Day I was accustomed to. Arriving back in Jerusalem it was dark. The town looked inviting, sitting in a crown of light on top of a hill. A few miles distant and clearly visible, the lights of Bethlehem on top of another hill. In the streets the pilgrims still strolled, tomorrow they would scatter to all parts of the world and they would relate stories of Christmas in the Holy Land.

— o —

The Refugee Stamp

IT was pouring rain when the postcard with the sunny views of Cyprus fell through my letter box. My friends were having a better time than me, they wrote, "weather hot, booze cheap, craic great." I was putting the card aside when my eye caught the drab little one cent black and white stamp beside its colourful thirteen cent neighbour. Above the words 'Refugee Fund' was a barefoot child sitting behind coils of barbed wire. In an instant I was taken back to a July morning in 1974 when Turkey invaded Cyprus and the events that followed gave birth to the stamp.

Cyprus had been my home for the previous year. I was there as part of a United Nations team attempting to maintain peace between Greek and Turkish Cypriots. We had been living on the edge of our nerves for weeks; in June Nicos Samson staged a coup against the government of Archbishop Makarios. Samson was in favour of Enosis — that is union with Greece — this gave Turkey the excuse it needed to invade the island, and so we sweated and waited. They will, they won't, and then suddenly we weren't wondering anymore. Living in Nicosia we were about eighteen miles from the Mediterranean, and it was as dawn broke on that July morning that the Turkish destroyers commenced their bombardment of the coastal defences.

The sound of the guns could be clearly heard in Nicosia. They didn't wake me, but they did wake my Greek Cypriot neighbours, and they came pounding on my door with an urgency of some magnitude. Few words were spoken, in my half awake state I followed them to the front of the house and then stood trying to focus my eyes towards the Kyrenia mountain range. Aircraft filled the sky, troop-carriers flying slowly, nose to tail, disgorging paratroopers from their bellies until the entire skyline was dotted with descending bodies. We couldn't see the defenders in the valley below us, but like ourselves they were having a rude awakening. At first we could hear a few shots as they scrambled to adjust to this plaque which had descended on them from the skies. Every few seconds brought another gun into life and some of the men from the skies were dead before they ever touched the ground.

Such moments are a mixture of fear and excitement, I stood there full with both emotions. The rising sun was removing the last vestiges of night cover, and so the bombers arrived. They flew low and fast with the sun at their backs and I could see the bombs in that brief space of time between release and target. The green line was the area between Greek and Turk that lay about five hundred yards in front of us and it was there all the action was taking place. There we stood like a theatre audience with a live war on stage before our eyes. Eventually common sense took over and we took ourselves inside, opened all the windows, to avoid flying glass, and filled the bath in case our water supply should be cut.

By eight that morning the battle was fully developed, palls of black smoke hung everywhere over the city and the air was sharp with the smell of gunfire and exploding bombs. We didn't feel safe where we were but it was too dangerous to move. My Greek neighbours were also aware of that danger, but they had heard such stories of what might happen to them at the hands of the Turkish soldiers that even though they weren't the bravest of people under God's sun, they still preferred to take their chances out there on the open road. What they couldn't pack inside their car, they tied to the roof, and like a mobile junk heap they headed for the mountains. Others were doing the same and by nightfall in our area of Ayios Dhometios, apart from ourselves and a few foreigners, the exodus was complete. The shooting eased and the war-planes made their last pass of the day before heading for their bases in Turkey. I went walking in the streets near the house, an eerie calm had descended, the street lights were gone, every house in darkness, not a soul in the area and only the odd sad howl of an abandoned dog or an occasional burst of gunfire. In the distance fires burned along miles of the Kyrenia mountain range, the flames gave a pink glow to the smoke making it appear like burning clouds in the clear night sky.

At dawn the next morning they picked up where they had left off, and for four days this pattern continued. Our supplies were running low, but otherwise our luck was holding. The water still flowed and as yet nothing had hit our house. Thoughts of total safety were slighly premature, our luck ran out and now the fighting was all around us. Bullets whizzed through the upstairs windows and fragments from a mortar bomb sent the glass in our front door flying into the house. We brought mattresses to the kitchen, built a little shelter, got down behind it, prayed, and waited. At mid-morning a ceasefire was agreed, the guns went silent and we came out nervously and inspected the damage to our house.

In that four days many had died, two hundred thousand were made homeless and the Turkish army had taken control of thirty six per cent of the island. The Greek Cypriots are a resilient people and very soon they were coping with the new problem of refugees. Among the measures taken was the introduction of the refugee stamp, one cent extra on every piece of mail. The drab little stamp with the sad faced child behind the wire still lives today, a source of revenue and a reminder of things past and the then as yet divided Island of Cyprus.

An Easter Sunday in Pakistan

EVER since childhood I had heard some people say that at sunrise on Easter Sunday morning the sun danced in the heavens. A few acquaintances said they actually witnessed the spectacle. I was always sceptical and on one occasion got up sufficiently early to test it. It was a waste of time, the only thing I saw that morning was big raindrops falling from the black clouds that hung like a leaking roof over the country.

Test number two was carried out far from Ireland. I wasn't up early just to check the sunrise, but around 4 a.m. on an Easter Sunday morning, myself, my friend and colleague Rauno Halme from Finland, his wife Ann from Australia and their small son, set out from Rawalpindi in Pakistan. We had a few free days in hand and we would more or less go where the road took us. This time we were headed south east, we would hit Jhelum and on towards Jammu on the Indian border. A few weeks earlier we had gone west, right into the mouth of the Kyber Pass and we only turned back when we were confronted by some menacing individuals carrying an assortment of weapons in the vicinity of the Afghanistan border. On that Easter morning we were on "the great trunk road" which runs right across the subcontinent. A very grandiose name for a road that is narrow, twisting and full of holes.

All the way, to the east of us, was hilly and barren terrain, stretching away in the far off distance to the Himalayas. And very soon from behind those hills in the east a red rim of light would appear. Rauno was driving, I could sit and watch the horizon with a hawk's eye. Up came the big red ball from behind the Indian hills, revealing the stark landscape. Only daybreak, yet there was movement everywhere. Villages had come alive, vegetable sellers sat beside their produce, cloaks wrapped tightly around them as protection from the cool air of early morning. In the villages the great trunk road was reduced to a mud track that ran between shanty houses whose walls were made of mud that had been baked in the roasting sun of high summer. A heavy rainfall of the previous day had turned the villages into mud ponds.

Up came the sun, nice and steady, off came the cloaks to meet the heat of the day, everything nice and steady, but most of all the sun, no jigs or reels. The Finn laughed at my superstition, while Ann was too busy trying to keep the young fellow from getting into the mud.

We pushed on and forgot about the non-dancing sun, and somewhere out in the middle of nowhere we stopped for breakfast, which we had with us in the boot of the car. We sat by the roadside eating, and within minutes a circle of young men gathered around us. They stood back four or five yards just looking, smiling and talking among themselves. It didn't take long to figure out their interest. Rauno was a blonde blue eyed Finn. Ann was a blonde, blue eyed Aussie. The little fellow, who was born in India, had a mane of long blonde hair, bleached white by the sun and a pair of ice blue eyes that pierced like laser beams. As we prepared to leave the onlookers ventured closer to examine and touch this alien child.

We got to Jhelum town around lunchtime. In a curious way it looked like a town from an old western movie. A few wooden buildings with balconies, men walking slow along dirt sidewalks, and of course the mud. Jhelum was a deliberate stop for me. We drove into the Presentation Convent, and within the red brick walls was a scene soft on my eyes. Trees, green grass and order. I hadn't spoken to an Irish person in months, and within minutes here we were sitting in the garden sipping tea with Sister Enda Carolan from Bailieboro, Co. Cavan, and Sister Eilish Heany from Co. Meath. We were joined by Father Pat Murray from Ashbourne. I recalled watching his brother, Brendan, playing football for Meath. It didn't take a lot of persuading to get us to stay for a meal. I hadn't seen an Irish person for months but I hadn't had an Irish meal for a year. As they say around my part of the country "we laid back our ears" and enjoyed an Irish stew. And I praised the day Irish nuns and priests went to far flung places. The Finn and the Aussie were licking their lips as well. It was also a long way from Melbourne and Helsinki.

Later that evening the Irish trio gave us a send-off as we again turned onto the great trunk road. The tall Father Pat was trying to wave at us with about half a dozen brown skinned, toothless waifs swinging out of him. Heading towards Jammu, Rauno wondered if I knew anyone there! "Yea," I said, I believe we'll find another Irishman, watch out for green grass and trees." The sun may not have danced for me that Easter morning, but it certainly did shine in Jhelum.

— O —

Changing House

THE first time I moved I had one suitcase and it was lightly packed. Preparation for the last move took days to get everything together. Being a compulsive collector the accumulated junk of half a lifetime was weighing me down. But it would be as hard to part with a piece of it as it would be to cut my foot off. There's an old saying that goes "act in haste repent at leisure." In my early days of shifting house the packing was often done in haste and to this day I'm regretting it with all the leisure in the world. Glass items came out in a thousand pieces, lamps that would never again throw light. A few pictures that had graced the wall of a room for the last time. You definitely live and learn. However, the hassle of packing is soon forgotten, it is merely the physical discomfort of an itinerant life. It is the uprooting of one from any place that has been home that leaves a little scar.

When the last item had been loaded on the truck and you walked back into the empty house and your footsteps echoed through the rooms as you did that last grand tour of the place that had been home for two or maybe three years, it was as if a little of you died there and then. Somewhere out there was a new country and a new home, a new sense of expectancy and adventure and hope. Tomorrow might bring all things new and wonderful, but today you were closing a chapter, pulling down the blinds at the sunset of one period. And along the walls of the empty rooms the outlines of the pictures that hung there. The curtainless windows letting in the harsh light of a middle eastern sky. In that few moments standing there, across the memory flashed a fast re-run of the previous years; a memory of that house on the slopes of the Mount of Olives in Jerusalem where we had a great party after the christening of our daughter; where one day suffering from a terrible toothache I drank whiskey for the first time and spent a lovely hour sitting on a rock in the garden seeing my surroundings as never before.

The house in Damascus had its moments too. Our son was born in that city and when he was two he pushed his pram at speed straight through the glass door that led to the garden. Thankfully glass fell everywhere but on him. We found a hedgehog in that garden and it stayed with us all the years.

When we had that house packed up to leave, we had a little hooley. There was an old piano there, which we had inherited from someone and that night a fellow Irishman played it beautifully. For a stool he sat on one of the empty packing crates with the lid left loosely on the top. Neither he nor the lid was very steady and he toppled into the box and the lid closed on top of him. And there he slept very well until morning and no one missed him. If anyone living there now is hearing a ghost playing "Danny Boy", I know who it is.

The house in Ayios Dhometios in Nicosia was my favourite of them all. The large windows, the polished wooden floors, the big stone fireplace. Orange and lemon trees in the garden and that lovely fragrance coming through the open windows in summer. Cyprus, the island of Aphrodite, leaves its mark on all who visit her and we were no exception. From picnics and singsongs sitting on the warm sand at Limassol to hours walking among the pines on top of the Troodos mountains. The Turks invaded the Island and for a while the birdsong was mute and the acrid smell of gunpowder took over from the pines and the lemon trees. But that too passed and the island got back to its business of welcoming tourists from all over the world. Costas, our local shopkeeper, came every day on his little motorcycle delivering the groceries. The day we were leaving Cyprus he called and brought us three bottles of good wine. This was a nice gesture since he was losing our custom anyway.

If I have an abiding memory of Cyprus, it isn't so much of the warm days and the sandy beaches. But I remember the smell of lemon trees, the chirping of crickets and I can see Costas sitting low on his motorcycle, put-putting through the narrow streets of Ayios Dhometios, his carrier bag full of groceries. When we moved house for the last time it was here in Dublin and it was only half a mile. For weeks our children kept going back to their friends at the old place and then gradually they made friends around the new house. The dust had settled on our wandering days.

— o —

An Arabic View of Ireland

WHERE are you from? the man asked me. He was standing beside me at a football match in Damascus. "Ireland," I said. "Ah, the land of the potato, and you have de Valera, yes?" he added. "You're right," I told him. He was pleased with himself at his knowledge. Their wasn't much point in telling him that we didn't have de Valera anymore, and that our reputation for potatoes nowadays was that we imported them, possibly even from his own country. He was now encouraged to pursue his knowledge of Ireland. "It is a very green country, yes?" I nodded agreement, it was getting hard to watch the football match and answer his questions.

He stuck with me as we left the football grounds, and when I stumbled on a discarded soft-drink can, he said, "everything in your country is very tidy, not like this, yes?" That did it, I now knew he didn't know much about Ireland. I could have told him that the reason I didn't break my ankle on that tin can was because my ankles were very strong from twisting regularly on tin cans in Ireland. Maybe he should have been advised that we are not so sure anymore whether Ireland is green or not, it's such a long time since we took a look under the rubbish to find out. My new found friend envied that vast amount of ocean we have around our country. "Very good for swimming and planty of fish, yes?" "The sea is a bit cold for swimming," I told him. Must be that someone put a weaker bulb in the lamp in the sky over our country than the one over his.

Would he have understood had I told him we had some of the strongest fish in the world, stronger even than my ankles. They had survived in polluted lakes and rivers. But it wasn't the bite a fish could take out of you that was the danger, so much as the bite you would take out of it. He wanted to know if we had sharks in the seas around Ireland. I told him we had no dangerous sharks in Irish waters. He laughed, although I don't think he got the point when I said we had lots of sharks that had legs and walked around. We got to the corner of Abu Romanie street when a motorist almost bowled us over. "Crazy," my friend said, "you don't have drivers like that in Ireland, yes?" My friend's ignorance was appalling. What was the use of telling him that the same driver in Ireland would have got the two of us.

Day Follows Night

When life has lost its purpose
And you're feeling really down.
When the smile that lit your face
Has been replaced by a frown.

When the hope that lived within you
Has been driven from your heart.
And the heavy weight of troubles
Keeps you and happiness apart.

Don't lie down and surrender
Get up and make a fight.
Remember that each dawning
Is preceded by a night.

When you need some consolation
Just walk along the shore.
Paddle in the tide of yesterday
As it comes rolling back once more.

Remember how it was last winter
When the icy wind bit your face.
And it's all now just a memory
Pushed behind by summer's warm embrace.

Stroll down by the woodlands
And remember the trees so lean.
Now see them fully covered
In their many shades of green.

Feast your eyes on flowers
And hear the humming of the bee.
Thank God that you're living
And life's most precious gifts are free.

The Will

A SHORT STORY

THE priest's words sounded like a verse he knew by heart, its only separate identity being the name of the deceased. "Her life could be an example to all of us. She cared well for her family, she helped her neighbours at every turn, and above all she paid special attention to her religious duties. She will be sadly missed by all of us, but especially by Paul."

The sound of his own name brought a rush of blood to his face. The priest's words seemed to drift away. For a few seconds he thought he was going deaf. He was fifty years old and he wanted to stand up and shout: "She was a bitch, a red-roaring bitch. There she is now, lying there in the coffin, rosary beads wrapped around her fingers, her eyes closed. The same way she so often looked when she was alive."

At the church door hands came at him from all directions. "Sorry for your troubles, Paul." He nodded acceptance to all, "thanks very much for coming." The rain poured down, drops as big as peas. His shoes stuck to the red clay. The raindrops rolled down his face and dripped off his angular jaw, falling on his mud-red shoes. The priest sprinkled holy water and it disappeared into anonymity among the little crystals that lay on top of the coffin.

Free at last, the thought struck him. But he was fifty, he couldn't roll back the years, take the pain from his shoulders or the grey from his hair. A wave of anger swept across him. He would have married when he was thirty. God knows Eileen Casey gave him every chance before she packed up and went to Boston. But the old lady wouldn't budge. The farm would be his when she died, "that was the way your father would have wanted it," she told him. He was only ten when his father was killed in the haggard by a bull. He didn't know what the hell his father would have wanted.

The room smelled of stale urine. Getting down on his knees he pulled from under her bed the old leather suitcase. The bottom was lined with a newspaper from 1936. The will was there, covering a picture of Jessie Owens at the Berlin Olympics. He held the will in his hand and stared hard at the black athlete. But it wasn't Jessie Owens he saw, it was Paul Coogan, full-back for Carrigeen Gaels. As a younger man he could really move, fielding that football so high they called him "Aeroplane Coogan". But that was the past, now his thoughts turned to Eileen. Christ, how he wished he had married her.

147

He sat back on his heels and looked at the bed, brass ends with big round knobs that she polished every week. The bed-clothes were tossed, the quilt half on the floor, just as she had left it. The wallpaper that had never been changed in his lifetime, and that awful floral pattern. He stood up and gave the suitcase a kick, and then another, and a third still harder one. It hurt his foot and he felt bad about kicking the case, but angry that it had hurt his foot.

He had been a real coward once, he should have gone to Boston with Eileen Casey. Leave the old lady and the farm to stew together. She didn't want Eileen, she didn't want any woman in the house. "You'll have time enough for that," she would say. Now he had that time, and with a worn-out fifty year old body with an arthritic shoulder and a house that belonged to the past. He should have forced her to make over the farm to him. He should have killed her. The thought crossed his mind for a few seconds and he quickly dispelled it.

Back in the big kitchen a black kettle steamed gently on the Aga cooker, a hen stuck an enquiring head through a half open door. A car passed on the road outside, then all was silent again, except for the ticking of the clock on the mantelpiece. That ticking seemed much louder now since he was alone. The shadows climbed up the wall as the sun dipped behind the conifers. Those trees were twenty years old, he was sure of their age, he planted them the month Eileen went to America. The trees had been a sort of countdown clock on his life. The crops came and went, the beeches and the oaks were licking the clouds since the day he was born, but that row of spruce climbed a little every year. Years of his life that had drifted away as quietly as a feather on the wind.

The farm hadn't marched with the times. A lot of Coogan's ways were the old ways, a little of this a little of that. Here too the old lady had her way. That was partly why he went to town on the bicycle the next morning. She could never understand why anyone would want to use petrol to drive to town when they could go on a bike. To avoid argument he cycled, unless the rain was cutting holes in the road.

This morning he was enjoying it. The sun shafted through the trees and gave him a sense of speed as he split the shadows that crossed the road. The tyres hummed and he pressed harder on the pedals, it was exhilarating. There was no pain in his shoulder. Peace and pleasure might sometimes come and last for a mile of road. For that brief period he was caught in a timewarp. He could be twenty and the world was before him and everything was possible, everything.

He rested the bike against the wall of George A. Stockwell's office. A big black, high nellie of a bike, no need to lock it, they only stole the racing types, with narrow tyres, and saddles that would cut the arse of you.

148

Stockwell was in his office. A fat man who grew fatter and lived well on the townspeople and the surrounding farms. Most of what he was paid for could be done far better by a decent letter writer.

Coogan pulled his mother's will from an inside pocket. "I want you to do whatever is necessary." Having looked up and down the document for a few minutes the solicitor looked over his glasses and spoke. "She left everything to you, we will take out probate," then adding, "it's a big job, it will take time." Stockwell was true to form, making work of out nothing was his trade mark.

Leaving the solicitor, he went to Kirwan's pub. He sat at the bar, ordered a pint and had a feeling of celebration. After fifty years he finally owned something. Two locals sat at the far end, dimly visible in a haze of smoke. "Pour whatever you're having yourself", Coogan said to the barman. The barman promptly filled a scotch, nodded thanks and slid the glass under the counter.

Four hours later Coogan was still there and the world was going out of focus for him. He told the barman that twenty years ago he wanted to marry Eileen Casey, but he couldn't, because of his mother, and he didn't have the farm. The barman told him he saw Eileen a few days ago, "she was in town, home on holidays, a bloody fine looking woman still," the barman said. Coogan felt a wave of depression settle on him like the black clouds that rested on the mountain. The barman leaned his elbows on the counter bringing his head closer to Coogan. "Why the hell didn't you marry her?" Coogan swallowed the last of his drink and keeping his eyes on the glass as he put it down said, "I had nowhere to bring her."

As he hopped from the bike at the gate it was just turning dark. The dog ran to him lashing his bushy tail against his leg. The unlit windows of the house stared at him like a pair of black eyes. He would have almost welcomed the admonition his mother would have given him, for the faint spark of life she would have brought to the house. Inside he turned on every light in every room and then went back outside to look. Feeling a little better he went inside again, inviting the dog in after him. The dog didn't hesitate, dashing past him to take up a place beside his chair.

Coogan paced up and down the kitchen, he opened presses and closed them again, looking for nothing in particular. His thoughts raced, he clenched his fists trying to concentrate, trying to find the source of this new and excessive restlessness. It was the barman's words, "why the hell didn't you marry her?" He knew she was at home and that didn't help either.

Joy at release from poverty and the shackles of his mother was short lived. Frustration from the memory of wasted years gripped him, he paced the kitchen faster, beads of sweat gathering on his brow. He looked at the Sacred Heart picture on the wall, and for twenty seconds he yelled as hard

149

as he could, until he felt his lungs would burst. Tidal flows of foul language rolled off his tongue, until fear of the dead and fear of God gripped him and he stopped. The dog, sensing the tension, stood up and barked.

With shaking hands he poured himself a stiff whiskey. He wanted to go to sleep, not for the rest, purely for the temporary oblivion. Tomorrow might be a better day. Walking up the stairs he was unsteady. He thought of his father, he wished he was alive. He would like to see him, to talk to him. He went into his mother's room and pulled the leather suitcase from under the bed. There was a photograph of his father in there somewhere among the assorted documents, recipes, letters and faded pictures. He smiled when he found it. The face with the strong jaw smiled back at him. A man in working clothes standing beside a horse. He wished the man could come alive and step from the picture, and together they would be a team. But reality was always a pace behind the heels of his dreams, and the heavy feeling in his chest made him take short breaths. He grabbed the suitcase, jerking it from the floor, scattering the contents all over the room. The newspaper with the picture of Jessie Owens landed on top. And from the folds of the newspaper a document slid onto the floor. His eye caught the fancy black print, standing bold against the white paper. 'Last Will and Testament'. Had she made another Will?, his heart raced. The handwriting wasn't hers. The signature was, Michael Joseph Coogan, his father. It was his father's Will, made forty two years earlier and hidden away by his mother. She had always said, "poor Mick died without leaving any will."

The Will left the farm to , "My son Paul when he attains the age of twenty-five years." There was provision for Paul's mother "to be taken care of for as long as she lives." He walked downstairs in a daze with the will in one hand. He finished the bottle of whiskey and lay for the night drunk on the kitchen floor. The dog lay beside him licking his face.

It was raining the next morning and he drove the Morris Minor to town. Red eyed and with rain running down his face he walked past Stockwell's secretary and into the big man's office. He placed his father's will in front of the solicitor. Three times he hammered his fist on the will, as if nailing it to the desk. Their eyes met, but nothing was said. Coogan turned and walked out.

The rain had stopped and a weak sun broke through the clouds. Walking across the street towards the pub he felt a lightness in his step and flickers of optimism flashed through his mind. There was still some life to be lived. The barman spotted him the second he entered the pub. Taking a damp cloth, he cleaned the little alcove under the counter where he kept his own glass.